The Child's Vanishing Landscape

Compiled by

Sue Cooke

Public Liaison & Information
Planning & Architecture Department

Sue Fenoughty

Environmental Education,
Advisory Teacher
Curriculum Support Service

Erica Pounce

History Advisory Teacher,
Curriculum Support Service

Birmingham City Council

First published by Brewin Books November1993

Birmingham City Council
Department of Planning
and Architecture

All rights reserved

ISBN 1 85858 029 3

British Library Cataloguing
in Publication Data

A catalogue record for this book is
available from the British Library

Designed and produced by
Birmingham City Council
Department of Planning and Architecture

Printed in Great Britain

CONTENTS

Sir Adrian Cadbury

*F*OREWORD

I was delighted to be asked to write a foreword to this imaginative book, because I have always been fascinated by the stories which buildings have to tell. There is so much to find out in who built them, who lived in them, who altered them and who perhaps knocked them down. The rise and fall of buildings also charts the changing shape of our particular neighbourhood and of the City as a whole.

I can trace my family history through Birmingham buildings. My great-great-grandfather, Richard Cadbury, came to Birmingham in 1794 and soon after he arrived he was elected a Street Commissioner. The Street Commissioners were the City Councillors of their day and Richard was involved in buying the Bull Ring land for the City and in building the Town Hall. Everyone now associates those two landmarks with Birmingham. They are a reminder of those who had the vision to see that their modest town would one day grow into a great City and built accordingly.

Richard's son John, who founded the Cadbury business, first manufactured cocoa in a warehouse in Crooked Lane, just off Bull Street. He had to move from there to make way for the building of the Birmingham and Oxford Railway line into what is now New Street Station. His next factory was in Bridge Street, not far away and still in central Birmingham. There the business flourished under his two sons, Richard and George, to the extent that they had to look for larger premises.

So it was that in 1879 the two brothers took the unprecedented step of building a new factory out in what was then the Worcestershire countryside. George planned the factory with the help of an architect and whenever he was not needed at Bridge Street, he would lend a hand with the actual building work at Bournville. Once when he was helping to tile the roof, he was told off in no uncertain terms for his lack of skill by one of the builders, who had no idea who he was!

You can plot the growth of the Bournville factory by picking out the different styles of building from 1879 to the present day. There are still parts of the original factory left, from them you can gauge the size and shape of the buildings which George Cadbury helped to plan and to build.

In addition to finding out about the history of particular buildings, it is interesting to look at the way in which neighbourhoods change their character, as different types of people with different styles of living move into them. Changing patterns of life determine the development of the City and remind us that conservation does not just mean preserving buildings as monuments, but also finding new uses for them which are in keeping with their past and with their surroundings.

This book has given enjoyment to those who wrote it as it will to those who read it; it has the virtue of being a continuing story to which all of us can add. What has been recorded cannot vanish without trace.

Adrian Cadbury

5

Launch of Birmingham's Conservation Strategy - Victoria Law Courts.
From left to right: Les Sparks, Director of Planning & Architecture, Birmingham City Council, Cllr Fred Chapman, Chair of Planning Committee, Jennie Page, Chief Executive, English Heritage

PREFACE

BY LES SPARKS
DIRECTOR OF PLANNING & ARCHITECTURE

BIRMINGHAM'S CONSERVATION STRATEGY

Birmingham is a modern city, renowned for its progressive approach over the last 200 years. But over that period it has acquired a wealth of history, much of it encapsulated in the buildings which have survived.

This record deserves to be preserved and commemorated, so that future generations can join in celebrating the city's history. The book you are about to enjoy documents facets of that history as described by today's children.

The people of Birmingham have often been criticised for neglecting, and even destroying their heritage. That is why a comprehensive Conservation Strategy is needed now to rescue many fine historic buildings and artefacts before it is too late.

Two of the key objectives of the Conservation Strategy launched in 1992 are addressed by this book. The first is to research and document the history of our architectural heritage. Too little is known about our old buildings, and their historic importance is often undervalued simply through our ignorance about them.

Secondly, the Strategy emphasises the importance of educating our young people to appreciate the heritage that surrounds them. All our efforts to preserve these buildings will be wasted if future generations fail to maintain them correctly or take sufficient interest in them.

Today's young people are growing up with a much keener interest in their surroundings and an awareness about the vulnerability of the environment. This book builds on that interest and helps to supplant vandalism and graffiti with civic pride and respect for the richness and beauty of our environment.

A Young person's introduction to Conservation of the built environment

This project originated from an idea by Sue Cooke to produce a book for children about the stories behind listed buildings (Conservation Strategy forBirmingham, Objective No 6). With the assistance of Curriculum Support Service, Education Department, a competition was promoted to all schools in Birmingham: 'Find a listed building, discover the facts and weave a story around those facts'. The winning entries are incorporated into this book, although many more superb entries were received.

What is a Listed Building?

A listed building is a building of special interest. Either because of its history, or because of the famous people who lived in the building, or because of the building's particular design. Birmingham has 1,725 listed buildings, ranging from mansions, law courts, schools and churches, to hovels, lamp posts, statues and bridges. They are put on to a national list by the Department of National Heritage, a government department which was set up to protect the future of these buildings.

There are three sorts of listed buildings. Grade I must be of exceptional architectural or historical interest such as the Town Hall. Grade II* are buildings which have to be of particular importance and more than special interest such as St Martin's Church in the Bull Ring. Grade II are usually buildings of special interest such as the restored cottages in Station Road, Erdington, whose history dates back to the 17th Century.

Jenny Colley and Chris Wilson from Osborne Junior and Infant School, Erdington taste life in the nineteenth Century with a visit to restored Grade II listed Cottages in Station Road, Erdington.

Birmingham has its own local list of special buildings.

Grade A, which are of national listing quality, such as the flats in Garrison Lane, Bordesley. Grade B, important in the City architectural or local street scene context, such as Acocks Green Fire Station, and Grade C, of local historical or industrial archaeological significance such as the British Gas gas holders in the Heartlands area.

What is a Conservation Area?

Some areas of the City of Birmingham, like Edgbaston, or Bournville or Four Oaks in Sutton Coldfield, have a large number of special buildings, grouped together. These areas are called Conservation Areas. Birmingham has 26.

If you live in a listed building or a Conservation Area and you want to make an alteration to your building, you will need to let the Local Planning Authority know what you want to do. They will be able to advise you of the best substances to use and whether your alterations fit in with the design of the building or the area. Listed Buildings are important because they are a constant reminder of the past. Without the buildings these memories are lost.

Sue Cooke
Public Liaison & Information
Department of Planning & Architecture

MAP SHOWING CONSERVATION AREAS & LISTED LEA SCHOOLS

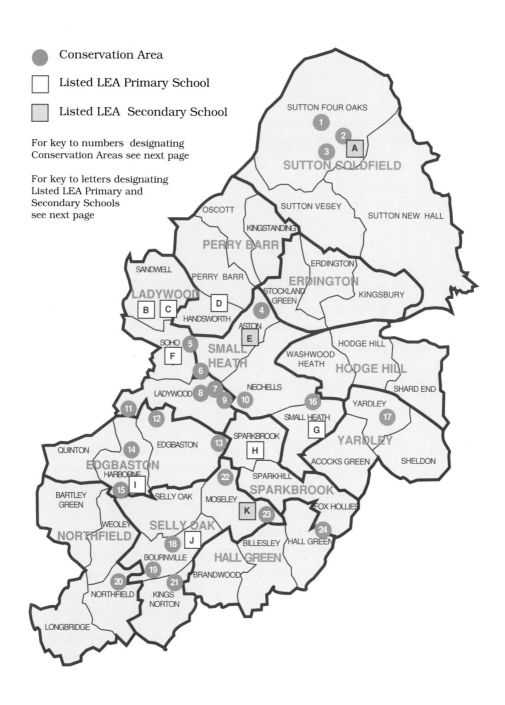

● Conservation Area

☐ Listed LEA Primary School

▨ Listed LEA Secondary School

For key to numbers designating Conservation Areas see next page

For key to letters designating Listed LEA Primary and Secondary Schools see next page

KEY Conservation Areas

KEY	CONSERVATION AREA
1	Four Oaks
2	Anchorage Road
3	Sutton Coldfield
4	Aston Hall and Church
5	Lozells
6	Key Hill
7	St Paul's Square
8	Jewellery Quarter
9	Colmore Row
10	Warwick Bar
11	Barnsley Road
12	St Augustine's
13	Lee Cres/RylandRd/Edgbaston
14	Moor Pool
15	Harborne Old Village
16	Ideal Village, Bordesley Green
17	Old Yardley
18	Bournville Village
19	Bournville Tenants
20	Northfield
21	Kings Norton
22	Moseley
23	St Agnes
24	School Road, Hall Green

KEY Listed LEA Primary & Secondary Schools

KEY	SCHOOL
A	BISHOP VESEY GRAMMAR SCHOOL
B	ROOKERY ROAD JUNIOR AND INFANT SCHOOL
C	GROVE INFANT SCHOOL
D	CANTERBURY CROSS JUNIOR AND INFANT SCHOOL
E	BROADWAY ANNEXE
F	BENSON JUNIOR AND INFANT SCHOOL
G	OLDKNOW JUNIOR SCHOOL
H	LADYPOOL JUNIOR AND INFANT SCHOOL
I	ST PETER'S C.E. JUNIOR AND INFANT SCHOOL
J	BOURNVILLE JUNIOR AND INFANT SCHOOL
K	MOSELEY SCHOOL

ACKNOWLEDGEMENTS

The Planning and Architecture and Education Departments, Birmingham City Council are especially indebted to the following people and organisations for their help, advice and support in the production of this book.

COMPETITION JUDGES

Carl Chinn - Community Historian
Trevor James - Senior Adviser, Education
Peter Leather - Historical Writer and Lecturer
Robert Tolley - President of Birmingham Architectural Association and Conservation Partner of S.T. Walker and Partners

COMPILERS:

Sue Cooke - Public Liaison, Department of Planning and Architecture
Sue Fenoughty - Advisory Teacher for Environmental Education,Curriculum Support Service, Education Department
Erica Pounce - Advisory Teacher for History, Curriculum Support Service, Education Department

SPONSORS

Barclays Bank
Birmingham Education Business Partnership and TEC
Dillons the Bookstore
Laing's Charitable Trust
Maxim Group
S.T. Walker and Partners
Wayland Publishers
The Young Historian Scheme.

DESIGNER

Sandra Hadley, Graphics Team, Planning and Architecture

PHOTOGRAPHERS

Jane Holt, Photographic Team, Planning and Architecture
Gareth Lewis,Photographic Team, Planning and Architecture

TYPISTS

Pauline Grey, Planning and Architecture
Jane Adcock, Planning and Architecture

ADVICE & INFORMATION

Peter Harding, External Funding and Promotions Manager, Education Department
Chris Hargreaves, Conservation Group, Planning and Architecture
Angela Weston, Teacher, Turves Green Secondary School
Dianne Egginton, Teacher, St. Joseph's RC J.I. School
John Harrison, Chartered Architect

APPENDIX COMPILATION by Sue Fenoughty assisted by

Marianne Baxter, Sutton Coldfield Library
Sue Cooke Public Liaison, Department of Planning and Architecture,
Mrs. P.J. Birkhill Handsworth Local History Society
Philip Henslowe, Bournville Village Trust Group
Peter Leather, Historical Writer and Lecturer
Richard Myall, Architectural Technician, Department of Planning and Architecture
Dr. Chris Upton, Local Studies and History, Central Library. Birmingham.

From left to right.

Back row: Dr. Carl Chinn, Peter Leather, Robert Tolley, Sue Cooke.

Front row: Sue Fenoughty, Dr. Trevor James, Erica Pounce.

Disclaimer

This book is published from information gathered from a variety of sources. Birmingham City Council holds no responsibility for any inaccuracies.

WEOLEY BORING?

BY PETER LEATHER
HISTORICAL WRITER & LECTURER

The ruins of Weoley Castle were so boring that I fell asleep there.

It was a beautiful sunny day, and all the greenery around made it easy to forget I was in the midst of suburban Birmingham. Sunbathing on the nice-smelling grass seemed a much better idea than wandering around the lifeless fragments of old stone walls.

Half-asleep and through arrow-slit eyes I began to see the place in a different light - the light of times past.

First there was the open clearing, known as Weoh-Leah, where the Anglo-Saxons came to worship their pagan gods. Then came the first castle, surrounded by a wooded palisade and deep ditch.

Next I thought I saw the medieval stone-masons building the great stone walls around me. Those were the days of feasting and fighting, banquets and battles.

They passed like a dream, to be replaced by a Victorian brick farmhouse with the castle ruins at its back. Beyond them was a newish canal - the Dudley - a sign that the industrial age had arrived. Finally I thought I saw men and women of this century - archaeologists - digging up the site to rediscover its past glories.

I woke up with a start. Perhaps Weoley Castle isn't such a boring place after all!

Weoley Castle
Possible reconstruction, circa 1424

illustration courtesy of Department of Archaeology and Ethnography, Birmingham City Museum

	STATUTORY LISTING	YEAR	COMMENT
Remains of Weoley Castle	Grade II & Scheduled Ancient Monument	Dates from 1264	Roger De Somery was licensed to crenellate his Manor House

LISTED BUILDINGS & ENVIRONMENTAL EDUCATION

Sarehole Mill

'All subjects of the curriculum have an individual contribution to make in developing environmental education, and, in its turn, environmental education enriches and brings new perspectives to those subjects.'

(NCC Curriculum Guidance 7: Environmental Education 1990)

Environmental Education is not an extra subject: it is a cross curricular theme in the National Curriculum. It comprises three linked components:-

- education about the environment (knowledge)

- education for the environment (values, attitudes, positive action)

- education in or through the environment (a resource)

EDUCATION ABOUT THE ENVIRONMENT

Knowledge and understanding of the built environment can be developed by looking more closely at the buildings around us. In particular, we can look at their design and construction, the types and uses of the buildings' materials, and how they have been affected by human activity, as well as by natural change.

Local listed buildings are an excellent study focus for school topics, and the stories behind them can be used as a starting point for spin offs into almost any area of the curriculum. Schools should have few problems in finding a listed building to research at first hand, with nearly two thousand in the north, south and central areas of the city; some pupils attend a school that is itself a listed building. Investigative and interpretative skills can be applied to examine clues to the building's past: Why was it built? Who designed it? Who built it? When was it built? Who used it? What was it like? How has it changed? Do I like this building? Why? By this stage, the building will already be telling its own story.

EDUCATION FOR THE ENVIRONMENT

A deeper understanding of listed buildings is gained through investigation, and an appreciation of some of the conflicts which can arise between aesthetic, utilitarian and economic considerations. Pupils will be able to make their own deductions and suggest ways of ensuring the caring use of the buildings which they value, based on the knowledge they have acquired.

Although most of us in this country live in the built environment, when the word 'conservation' is mentioned, there is a tendency to think of issues affecting the natural environment. Saving threatened species and their natural habitats is vital; there is the need, too, to conserve some of our built 'habitats' - old buildings and structures with their stories, associations and roots in the past, which help to give an area its identity, and are the heritage of future generations. When Sarehole Mill fell into decay, the author J R Tolkien contributed to the fund to preserve it. The mill was part of the landscape he knew so well as a child living in Birmingham, and today's children can still visit the mill, described in his novel 'The Hobbit'.

EDUCATION IN OR THROUGH THE ENVIRONMENT

The emphasis of environmental education should be on enquiry and investigation by the pupils themselves, by direct experience wherever possible. Earlier this year, stimulated by the challenge to find stories behind listed buildings, pupils all over the city were out researching, at the same time coming into contact, maybe for the first time, with the building associated with their story. By stepping into the environment outside the classroom to find their stories, they widened their experience by interviewing and questioning people from many walks of life: planners, architects, builders, industrialists, archivists, clergymen, hoteliers, shopkeepers, park rangers, journalists, as well as householders.

The process of story researching has raised the schools' awareness of the rich variety of buildings in the city that can be used as a stimulus to learning across the curriculum. Pupils have discovered that many buildings with interesting stories attached have since vanished, or are under threat. This has heightened their interest in the conservation issues surrounding those that remain.

Sue Fenoughty, Environmental Awareness Advisory Teacher, Curriculum Support Service, LEA Birmingham

History, Environmental Education & Citizenship, A National Curriculum Perspective

It is through history that pupils can understand why it is important to conserve the built environment. In history pupils study the impact of humans on the environment and they look at environmental change and can reflect on the importance of preserving the historic landscape.

Throughout National Curriculum History pupils have to use buildings and sites as historical sources for finding out about the past. Even young children at infant school are now visiting old buildings to try to understand more about what it was like to live in a time that no one alive today can remember. As pupils in junior and secondary school study periods in history, they learn about the architecture of people in the past and the legacy which they have left us today.

Junior school children are now required to study a unit on local history. Much of the work is being developed around the immediate locality of their school and often involves researching old buildings in the area. Many children are being educated in listed school buildings and can use evidence to trace back to the children who sat in the same classrooms over a hundred years ago.

Perhaps the greatest resource for Birmingham youngsters is the city itself. At junior and at secondary level, pupils study Victorian Britain. They can easily relate the local buildings to national history. Examples of homes, rich and poor, public buildings, factories, churches, schools, pubs and theatres are clearly in evidence and can form a real basis for work on nineteenth century Britain.

In National Curriculum history pupils are also required to research, to collect and record information and to present their results. The local built environment offers tremendous potential for this.

History helps pupils to make sense of their present environment by looking at the past. It is essential that teachers equip pupils to respect, to appreciate and to try to preserve their heritage. The aims of environmental education are to encourage pupils to think for themselves on environmental issues, to question decisions, to make their views known and to respect the views of others.

Curriculum Guidance 8 on Citizenship takes this approach a step further. It encourages pupils to become participative members of their community. In environmental issues this means helping pupils to know how they can take action in future, for their future.

Erica Pounce
History Advisory Teacher
Curriculum Support Service
LEA, Birmingham

NATIONAL CURRICULUM HISTORY REQUIREMENTS USING THE BUILT ENVIRONMENT

HISTORICAL SOURCES

Pupils should have opportunities to learn about the past from a range of historical sources including:
- Buildings and sites

ATTAINMENT TARGETS

Especially AT3:

The use of historical sources
- Acquiring evidence from sources
- Forming judgments

HISTORICAL ENQUIRY & COMMUNICATION
- Investigating historical topics
- Selecting & Organising historical information
- Presenting knowledge in a variety of ways

STUDY UNITS

The study of Architecture is in each history core study unit at key stage 2 and 3.

KS3 - MEDIEVAL REALMS
- Architecture & how it reflected society

KS2 & KS3

TUDOR & STUART TIMES/THE MAKING OF THE UK

KS2
- Town & country life
- Architects & their buildings

KS3
- The impact on the architecture of political & religious change
- Social classes
- Regional differences

KS2 & KS3

VICTORIAN BRITAIN/TRADE EXPANSION & INDUSTRY

KS2
- Houses
- Public buildings
- Growth of factories
- Education
- Growth of towns

KS3
- How architecture reflected the growth of Industry & Empire & Popular Culture

KS2

BRITAIN SINCE 1930
- Industrial changes
- Environmental concerns
- Religious changes
- Changes in architecture

KS2-LOCAL HISTORY

Any aspect of the local community

KEY STAGE 1- HISTORY

At Key Stage 1 pupils should be given opportunities to develop an awareness of the past and how it was different from the present and should be introduced to historical sources, including buildings and sites.

Buildings in the local environment are an excellent starting point for young children, they are a valuable source to learn from in themselves but also act as an introduction to other historical sources such as artefacts, pictures and photographs and adults talking about their own past.

Children are required to progress from familiar situations to those more distant in the past. Buildings such as houses, shops, schools, cinemas and places of worship provide an excellent stimulus for looking at the everyday life, leisure and culture of people in the past.

At Key Stage 1 children should have opportunities to investigate.

- Changes in their own lives and those of their families or adults around them.
- Changes in the way of life of British people since the Second World War.
- The way of life of people in a period of the past beyond living memory.

A visit to an historic building is the most successful way of helping children to learn how people lived in the distant past.

Young children can see changes all around them in their immediate environment as old buildings are demolished and are replaced. Reflecting on these changes may help children to realise that their landscape is vanishing.

In National Curriculum history people should also be helped to develop an awareness of the past through stories, including myths and legends, stories about historic events, eye witness accounts and fictional stories about the past. Buildings provide an excellent start for a story, either the story of a visit to a local building or a story based around the history of a building based on historical evidence or rumour.

In National Curriculum history, children develop and demonstrate their knowledge, understanding and skills through the attainment targets.

For Attainment Target 1 looking at old buildings should help pupils to:-

- develop the language relating to the passing of time
- sequence events, perhaps through a story
- see why events happened
- observe differences in ways of life at different times in the past

For Attainment Target 2 looking at stories about old buildings should help pupils to:-

- develop an awareness that there are different ways of representing past events
- distinguish between different accounts of events

For Attainment Target 3 using buildings as an historical source for investigation should help pupils to:-

- find out more about the past
- talk about what they have found out
- make deductions about the past from evidence

At Key Stage 1 pupils are encouraged to ask questions and to communicate their awareness, looking at buildings provides a context for investigation. Stories about buildings are an invaluable stimulus. Retelling a story based around a building is an excellent way of allowing children to communicate their historical knowledge.

Erica Pounce
History Advisory Teacher
Curriculum Support Rervice
Birmingham LEA

BREARLEY STREET NURSERY

Picture drawn by:
Emma Cumisky, Bianca Jowhine,
Leanne Sheehan, Joel Jackson

THE BUILDING

This is an unusually advanced work by William Benslyn, a local government architect in the thirties. The constraints of a small site backing onto a factory has shaped the design. He doubles the accommodation by a second storey - unusual for a nursery, which seems to defy the slum surroundings and lifts up into the light and air. This particular solution is probably unique. The wide spaces between columns are achieved using a reinforced concrete floor and roof and 'gave freedom of planning'. A similar structure for a house design was already published in the English edition of Le Corbusier's book "Towards a New Architecture", the Domino House. Benslyn designed the Gaumont Cinema, now demolished, which was sited in Colmore Circus and was a fine example of Art Deco.

I like school

I like school,
Because its cool

I like school,

When i play ball,

I like school,

But i want to go to
the swimming pool.

Poem by:
Leanne Sheehan, André Harvey, Greg Walker,
Aaron Roberts-Lawler

	STATUTORY LISTING	YEAR	COMMENT
Brearley Street Nursery School, Brearley Street Hockley	local listing only	1939	By W.T. Benslyn Innovative concrete cantilevered construction

RADAR & THE CHAMBERLAIN TOWER

BY ALEXANDER SMITH
AGE 6 YEARS
HALLFIELD INFANT SCHOOL
EDGBASTON

I am a lecturer and I am 34. I am interested in radar. I use radar to find planes. Mark is my boss. It is 1940. I am doing experiments and I keep climbing up Joe to do them. It is very rainy. Joe is a clock tower. Its proper name is the Chamberlain Tower. It is for Joseph Chamberlain. It is 325 feet (99.06metres). The face is 17 feet 3 inches (4.11 metres) in diameter. The circumference is 54 feet 2 inches (16.52 metres). My estimate of the hour hand is 10 feet 8 inches (3.24 metres).

Birmingham University Clock Tower

	STATUTORY LISTING	YEAR	COMMENT
Chamberlain Tower University of Birmingham	Grade II	1900-1909	Designed by Sir Aston Webb & Ingress Bell

SELLY OAK CENTRE

Selly Oak Centre

George Cadbury built the
Selly Oak Institute in
Bristol Road in 1884
It was to be used for
Social clubs, reading
billiards and other activities
It was aimed at being
the centre of local life
and still is today.
Next year the centre celebrates
it's centenary.
The pictures show
George and Elizabeth Cadbury
1913 and the Selly Oak Centre.

|||≡|||≡|||≡|||≡|||≡|||≡|||≡

JIben

We looked at the
Selly Oak centre in Bristol
Inside I went Upstairs I saw
a big window with
Patterns on the glass

ⁿⁿⁿⁿⁿⁿⁿⁿⁿⁿⁿⁿⁿⁿⁿⁿ

Selly Oak Centre

Junaid

I drew the door.
It had a star
pattern

Junaid Y1

21

Children from Tiverton Infant School

Pritam Dey

We went out side and crassed the Road and to the park and went on the playground tran and we drew the out Side of the building and the building was black and Whilte and there was criss cross patterns at the top 'in' bxxt and White.

—||—||—||—||—||—||—||

Norazrina Samsudin

We went to look at the selly Oak Center in Bristol Road.
We went to the office we ask the woman how old the building was the woman said is 99 years old there was a wooden staircase and I drew a staircase.
One post was small and another was tall. There was a pattern onit They were brown.

	STATUTORY LISTING	YEAR	COMMENT
Selly Oak Centre	Grade II	Late 19th Century	An unusual Arts & Crafts timber framed building

22

KEY STAGE 2 - HISTORY

At Key Stage 2 pupils should have opportunities to learn about the past from a range of historical sources, including buildings and sites. In addition an awareness of the architecture of the period is required in each of the six core study units:- Invaders and Settlers, Tudor and Stuart Times, Victorian Britain, Britain Since 1930, Ancient Greece and Exploration and Encounters. Studying architecture is a wonderful way of finding out how people lived, their developments, their attitudes and their aspirations. For example by looking at any local Victorian buildings, a church, a school, public baths, a factory or a town hall, pupils can learn much about the culture, society and policies of the time.

Also at Key Stage 2 pupils are given opportunities to study an aspect of local history. Local buildings can be central to that study perhaps with supplementary information through local records, memories, pictures and photographs to look at changes through time. Every building, of course reflects a wider national trend and often is representative of an important historical issue, so meeting the requirements in the history orders. A study of a local building can give pupils the opportunity to investigate an historical topic, to select and organise the information and to communicate the results of the research.

It is through the history Attainment Targets that pupils develop and demonstrate their knowledge, understanding and skills. Local buildings are a relevant way of meeting some of the statements of attainment:-

- Appreciating change through time (AT1)*
- Making connections between different periods in history (AT1)
- Looking at different versions of the past through stories about people associated with buildings (AT2
- Making deductions and extracting information from the building itself (AT3)

It is important however when using stories in history that a distinction is made between fact and fiction. Successful use of story in history helps pupils to better understand the motives of people in the past in the context in which they lived. Stories about buildings need to be based firmly on historical evidence, but help pupils to hypothesise about cause and effect or to see why certain decisions may have been taken in the past.

Erica Pounce
History Advisory Teacher
Curriculum Support Service
Birmingham LEA

THE LITTLE CHURCH ON THE HILL
-A STORY ABOUT ST JOSEPH'S RC CHURCH

BY DIANNE EGGINTON
TEACHER
ST JOSEPH'S RC J.I. SCHOOL
NECHELLS

BACKGROUND

It was the year 1850 when the Roman Catholic community in Nechells decided that they needed their own chapel for funeral services. An architect called Augustus Welby Pugin was asked to design the chapel and work was soon under way. (Augustus Pugin later became very famous for working on designs for the Houses of Parliament). The first regular priest was Father Henry Fornby who came from St Chad's Cathedral to say mass.

FATHER GREANEY'S STORY

"It wasn't long though before the parish began to grow and by 1870, I, William Greaney as Parish Priest, realised that we would need a bigger place to worship. I knew that a new church would cost a lot of money and began to think of ways to raise the funds needed and finally had the idea to hold a Grand Bazaar.

The people from the parish were excited by this idea and we held lots of meetings to get everything organised. It was going to be a special occasion for everyone. As Augustus Pugin had died, his son Edward Pugin designed the extension to the chapel. After a lot of arrangements we decided that we would hold a bazaar in the Town Hall. I remember we planned so many fund-raising events, stalls, games and raffles that we had to book the Town Hall for six days.

The opening day arrived and there was a great deal of excitement. The Town Hall was soon full of noise and bustle. The news quickly got round that the Pope had sent a cameo brooch and a silver medal from Rome. We used these prizes in the raffle. Straight away the tickets began to sell. At the end of the bazaar we drew the raffle and Mr. Fulford and Mr. Smallwood were the proud owners of the medal and the brooch. The whole bazaar was a great success and the final amount raised came to £656.

I remember watching as the first brick was put into place in July 1871 and Bishop Ullathorne came to Nechells exactly a year later on the feast day of St. Joseph's to officially open the church. He commented on the splendour of the day, particularly his pleasure at hearing his favourite music -Haydn's Mass No 3. The people of the parish and myself were all very pleased that we had each played a part in building our new church."

	STATUTORY LISTING	YEAR	COMMENT
St. Joseph's Roman Catholic Church Thimble Mill Lane	Grade II	1850	Mortuary Chapel by AWN Pugin

From left to right, Keiran Edwards and Kelly Lawson, pupils at St. Joseph's Junior and Infant School have a taste of Victorian life as they study their local church, St. Joseph's in the Heartlands area of Birmingham.

BLAKESLEY HALL

BY ZAHEED IQBAL
YEAR 3
ARDEN J.I. SCHOOL, SPARKHILL

Somebody was coming and the person who was coming was Aylmer Foliot. Then I realised I was in Blakesley Hall at the time of the Tudors. The second thing I realised was that I was a lord. Then along came a servant with soup. I said "I do not like soup", so the servant went and got me apple juice, cheese and eggs and vegetables. I never ate the vegetables. Then I called the servant to go and scare the birds from the crops. After I had eaten I felt thirsty so I called the servant. I said "Try to get me some small beer".

I went for a walk around Blakesley Hall. First I went to the Great Hall, it was really dark. So I had to light a rush light. Then I called the servant. I said "light the fire". Because it was all cold it took the servant a long time.

Then I went to the parlour, that was a lovely room. The Great Hall and the parlour were the most important rooms. There was a bird hanging in a cage from the ceiling. There was a table which you could make longer. There was a little table. I had a diary and wrote with a quill pen in it.

It was getting dark so I had to go to bed. Before I went to bed I had to wash. It was my first wash for a long time. I shouted for a servant and said "Get me some cold water". When I had had my wash I told the servant to get out and not bother me. Then I snuggled into my warm little bed.

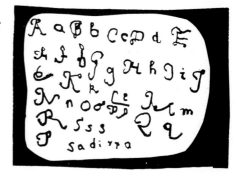

Note: Cover picture of Blakesley hall painted by Hanifa Mohammed.

	STATUTORY LISTING	YEAR	COMMENT
Blakesley Hall Blakesley Road Yardley	Grade II*	16th Century	Timber framed farmhouse built by Richard Smallbroke

MARY SIMMS OF ST. CYPRIAN'S CHURCH

BY JOANNE BLACKWELL
YEAR 5
REDHILL J.I. SCHOOL

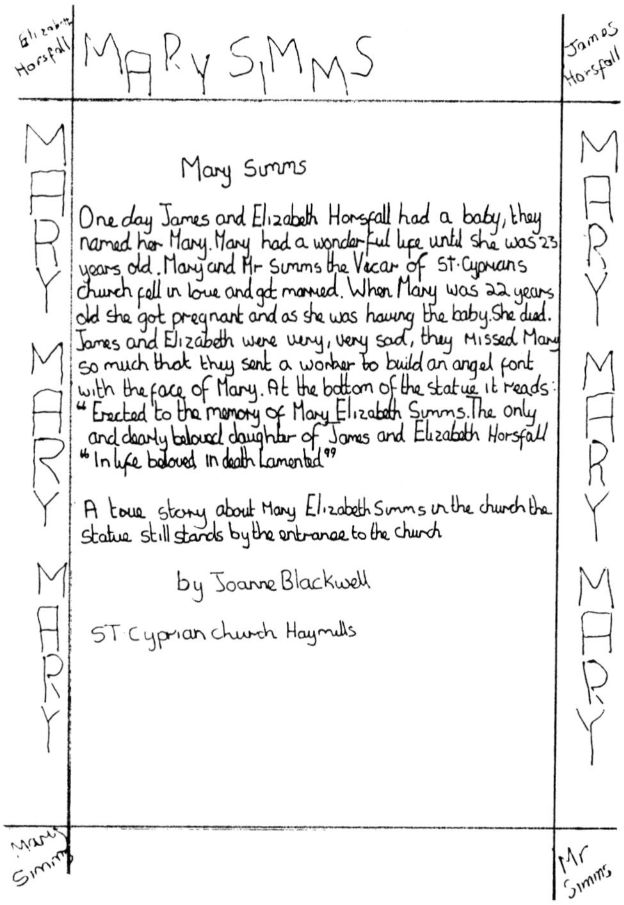
Elizabeth Horsfall
MARY SIMMS
James Horsfall
MARY MARY MARY
MARY MARY MARY

Mary Simms

One day James and Elizabeth Horsfall had a baby, they named her Mary. Mary had a wonder-ful life until she was 23 years old. Mary and Mr Simms the Vicar of St. Cyprians church fell in love and got married. When Mary was 22 years old she got pregnant and as she was having the baby. She died. James and Elizabeth were very, very sad, they missed Mary so much that they sent a worker to build an angel font with the face of Mary. At the bottom of the statue it reads: "Erected to the memory of Mary Elizabeth Simms. The only and dearly beloved daughter of James and Elizabeth Horsfall "In life beloved in death Lamented"

A true story about Mary Elizabeth Simms in the church the statue still stands by the entrance to the church

by Joanne Blackwell

ST Cyprian church Haymills

Mary Simms
Mr Simms

James Horsfall, 'ironmaster', moved his firm's wire drawing business from Penns Hall, Sutton Coldfield (see Appendix) to its present site in Hay Mills in 1859. The following year, he built a schoolroom for the education of the children of his workpeople, which was subsequently converted into a chapel. A Chaplain was appointed, Rev G H Simms, in 1866 and he married Mary Elizabeth, only daughter of James and Elizabeth Horsfall. The chapel was incorporated into the building of the new church of St Cyprian's which opened for worship in 1874 (see Appendix). Tragically, the chaplain's young wife died, and the Horsfall family added the mortuary chapel in 1877 in her memory.

The grave of Mary Simms

Two years later, they also presented the marble font to the church and it is said that the face of the angel on the font was modelled on their beloved daughter, Mary Elizabeth. Today, the descendants of James Horsfall, continue to give their support to the church.

	STATUTORY LISTING	YEAR	COMMENT
Church of St. Cyprian & St. Chad Hay Mills	Grade II	1873-4	Built by James Horsfall, Mill owner Designed by Martin & Chamberlain

Joanne Blackwell outside St. Cyprian's church, Hay Mills

ROUND THE ROUNDHOUSE

BY JOHN KEENE
AGE 8 YEARS
NELSON J. I. SCHOOL, LADYWOOD

Mr Bartlam came and took us to the Roundhouse. Mr Bartlam told us that it was a boat place. The boats were pulled by horses. They slept in the stables in the Roundhouse. We looked through the gate and saw the Roundhouse but we weren't allowed in because there was an alarm on the gate.

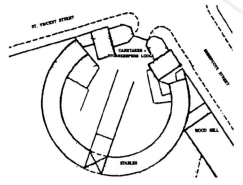

We went around on the bridge and Mrs Cowley took some groups to draw the Roundhouse. I drew a picture of the Roundhouse. Then we went back around to the bridge. We saw a horse coming towards us. It was pulling a barge. We fed the horse with carrots and hay. Then we lined up on the side and we got on the boat but then the man said stop because he had to put the steps on and open up the door.

Then we got on. We were sinking all the time. Then we moved. The horse got blocked by a bike which means he couldn't go on and he turned around and went back. Two men had to pull the boat and it kept on bumping on the side. Then we had to turn around. We couldn't turn round so they got a pole. They turned us around with it by pushing it against the boat. There was another boat coming this way. Then I fell asleep because I was worn out.

We were stuck in the middle of the water and couldn't get out, I went under the seat and changed into my Super Hero clothes. I had some red shoes on and an "S" sign on my silk shirt and a boat on my shoes. I got out from underneath the seat and made sure no-one saw me.

First I took out the girls. I flew and put them on the pathway. Then I flew back to the boat and took the boys back. Then I picked up the boat and put it down on the bridge. I unpolluted the water. I made a big massive tank and put the fat tube in the water and sucked up all the fuel and rubbish and everyone sunbathed and swam in the water. Then everyone was sad because I had to leave.

Then I granted Sindy's wish and made the Roundhouse into a farm. Then I had to leave. I went to Sindy and told her what I had done. Sindy went to the Roundhouse and said hurray.

Nicholas Wright, Year 3, Nelson J.I. School makes notes on the Round House
Photo courtesy of Norman Bartlam, Housing Education Officer, Ladywood Arts & Leisure Centre

27

*Aerial view of the Roundhouse showing its
distinctive horseshoe shape*

Today

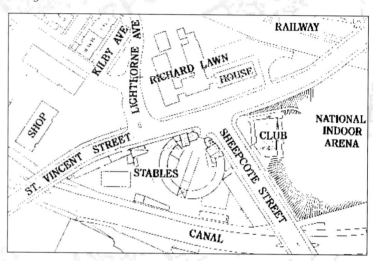

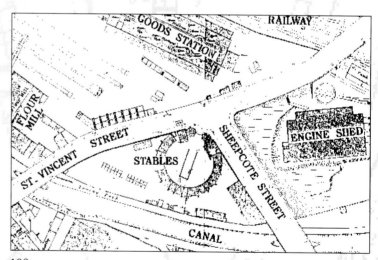

100 years ago

	STATUTORY LISTING	YEAR	COMMENT
The Roundhouse Sheepcote Street Ladywood	Grade II*	1840	Built for London & North Western Railway as a mineral & coal wharf

My Granny in the Jewellery Quarter

BY VICTORIA ALLEN
COLMERS FARM J.I. SCHOOL
BRISTOL ROAD SOUTH

My granny, Kate May Argyle, started work in what is now a listed building in St Paul's Square, Birmingham. Many of the places she worked at in the 1920's and the 1930's are still standing today, and are listed buildings. Her story is a typical story of a jewellery quarter worker who lived in the Jewellery Quarter area for some time.

This story is about the life of my granny when she worked and lived in the Jewellery Quarter. In 1922 she got her first job from the Education in Margaret Street. Her and another girl, whose father worked there already, were sent to Broughtons. They got the job. There were only those two applying for it at the time. She started work when she was fourteen at Broughtons in St Paul's Square and it is still there, but it is not a jewellers now.

When she had her first day there she liked it so much that when she got home for dinner she was eager to get back in the afternoon. She made "Alberts", which were men's watch-chains. (Albert, the Prince Consort, brought those into fashion). When my granny was making the chains, she had a few links that were loose that she joined together by soldering but the one thing was that she had to be careful that they did not roll up into balls when they were too hot. When she first got there it did not matter if it happened because she was learning. She had silver to start with, not gold. They had to be twisted, then after that they had to be taken to the foreman, and if they broke the foreman "didn't half look at you". The foreman twisted them to see if they would break and then she'd have to go back and re-do them if they broke. She also made women's necklaces which were tedious and very tiring to make. She had to pick up two pairs of pliers and she picked up the link and linked them together. She soldered it and picked up another one and soldered it and picked up another one and carried on. She had to do so many inches according to how long they wanted the necklace. She only did chains, but other parts of the factory did other things, diamond rings, bracelets and watches.

She worked from eight o'clock in the morning until six o'clock in the afternoon. She only had a break in the afternoon. Dinner time was from one o'clock until two o'clock. She used to run all the way home up George Street to Edward Street, and her mother always had a cooked dinner ready for her when she got home, which was rabbit stew or something like a piece of beef and roast potatoes and a pudding. They had hooters called "bulls" to tell them to come back to work and then the hooter would go again to say that the gates are closing and once the gates are closed she could not get in and she could not get out. If they were locked out they would not get paid.

She had to work on Saturday mornings from eight until twelve, mid-day. She was paid per day not piece work. Piece work is where you get paid for every item you make. Some of the others were paid piece work, but granny was not because she was not old enough. She never got onto piece work before Broughtons closed. When she was fourteen she was earning eight shillings a week. She only got a rise if she asked for it. She could not bear to ask but her mum kept telling her to ask seeing as though she had been there twelve months. In the end when she asked she only had a shilling rise. She had to give her mother all her money that she earned at work and she had sixpence back for pocket money. Her mum bought her her clothes and her food. For sixpence she could buy sweets and go to the pictures for tuppence. A few times she and Alice would go to a dance at a social place. When her sister, Alice, started work, Alice had a shilling pocket money and her mother raised granny's pocket money to a shilling. At the age of eighteen she had her own wages and had to give her mother so much. She never went to jewellers school in Newhall Street but some of the others did. Broughtons went bankrupt so they closed down.

She lived in a back-to-back house in Edward Street. It had two attics, one bedroom and one living room. The toilets were outside. The wash house was outside as well. She had to get all the water from outside because they didn't have any taps. In the summer granny's mum did the washing outside in the wash-house and in the winter they did the washing on the table. She slept in the attic with her sister, Alice. Her mum and dad slept in the bedroom underneath with Ann, the baby, in a cot. It was an iron cot, not a wooden cot like we have now. When Ann was older, she slept away from her mum and dad and she slept with granny in the bedroom in the attic. Granny had a double bed - iron with brass knobs.

When Broughtons closed down she went over the road to another job called Neils, in George Street, where they made combs and silver-backed hairbrushes. She worked in a big high building and she worked on the top. There were other factories underneath. It is still there but the little shops at the side have gone. The work frightened her

there because they had to put on a blowlamp to solder and if she left it too long it would roll up into a red-hot ball.

When she was working at Neils she moved house because her little sister had rheumatic fever. They moved to Geraldine Road, Yardley, where there was clean air, fields and farms, unlike where she was living before. In Geraldine Road her sister got better. The house cost about one hundred pounds. Her dad paid for it. He was a window cleaner. He didn't clean houses, he cleaned banks and things like that.

She travelled to work by tram from Hay Mills bridge. The trams were cold and rattley. They didn't have doors to close and they were all open. They had no heating in them. On the trams the seats were hard and facing one another. In the summer granny liked to go upstairs because it was nice and warm. The tickets were not paper they were cardboard. The conductor had tickets on one side and the money on the other side of him. When the conductor took the tickets out of the machine it went ding. When she bought a ticket she bought a workmans return. It cost thru'pence from Hay Mills. When she came back on the tram the conductor "dinged" the ticket and put a hole in it, to say that she'd paid. The ticket had a big "W" on it for workman. She always had a workmans return ticket. There were some returns for tuppence. The trams were the ones with the wires on and with the tracks. When the pole came off the wire the conductor would try to put it back on the wire and there would be blue sparks coming out and she would be cursing it as she would be late for work. When she was delayed she would have to run all the way to Camden Drive. When the trams were got rid of they had trolley buses - these were the ones that had overhead wires but no tracks. Sometimes the men would be driving their cattle to the slaughterhouse in Digbeth, and they would get in the way and she would be late again for work.

	STATUTORY LISTING	YEAR	COMMENT
Jewellery Quarter Conservation area	Designated as a Conservation area in 1980		

TIME TELLS A TALE

THE STORY OF BOURNVILLE JUNIOR SCHOOL

Extracts from the story written by five pupils in 6B

MICHAEL CHILTON
THOMAS DARVILL
CORRINE DAVIES-GRIFFITH
JON HUSKISSON
KATY WATERSTON

('Most of the information in this story is factual, having been taken from the school's Log Book and Punishment Books. We did, however, do some research into events that were mentioned').

I'm the Bournville Junior School clock. Today is the 1st of March 1993 and I'm just about to chime for the 4,953,780th time; wait a second. There. Right, now I'll tell you my story, but before I start, here's a drawing of me. Oh, by the way, I hope you notice the words underneath me because they are very important. The words CARPE DIEM are Latin and mean CATCH THE DAY, ie DON'T WASTE TIME, VALUE EVERY MOMENT OF THE DAY.

Bournville Junior School

George Cadbury put them on me so everyone would take notice and try to do what it says. To start my story, let's go back to 1905. The school is being built. George

Cadbury built the school, you'll probably recognise the name Cadbury. He decided to build the school because his workers needed somewhere to send their children. I've often wondered where they went before that! He built it well, it has a carillon on top which now has 48 bells and plays a tune every quarter of an hour. Years ago the children sang to the tunes, as responses to prayers.

Music score 'These are the tunes that the bells play every quarter of an hour').

31

The date today is 1st March 1939. I can remember I was all by myself because the school was closed. King George V and Queen Elizabeth were visiting Birmingham. All the children and villagers lined up on the Green to wave to the King and Queen. Oh, I just made a rhyme and I didn't even notice.

Main entrance 1906 By Jon Huskinsson

On the night of 23rd March 1939, Dr Innes came to the school to have a meeting with parents discussing evacuation in case of an emergency. You see, something called a war was looming because of a nasty little man called HITLER! Four days later letters went out asking parents if they wanted their children to be evacuated. I hoped a war wouldn't start so then the children wouldn't have to be evacuated. On 31st March, the head teacher announced that 261 children, can you believe it, were to be evacuated if necessary. (Mrs Bennett, who now works here, was one of the children who was evacuated).

On 26 August there was a national crisis, and all the teachers were called in to be given information that could be passed on to parents about evacuation. During the following three days children came to school

for rehearsals at 7.30am..... If war did start it was thought that large cities like Birmingham would be bombed by the Germans and that children would be safer in the countryside.

Sadly, the date is 1st September 1939, the day the evacuees are leaving for the country. It was early in the morning when they left and I cried as I saw them getting on the train at Bournville Railway Station.

Evacuees on railway station
Photo courtesy of Alton Douglas, Author of
Birmingham at War volume I.

The date is now 26th February 1940, the head teacher arrived back to school today leaving 95 children with teachers in safer places in the countryside after being with them since September. 230 children altogether were evacuated in September. The teachers started home teaching in October and said it was a great success. School was opened after requests from many parents. The head said yes, but only if parents wouldn't come to school when there was an air raid attack.

It is the 27th February and the first day of the war term began today. There was one class out of 12 which consisted of 58 children!! Children had to bring gas masks every day because they had to test them out twice a week.

On the 12th August 1940 the headmaster died in an operation to make the tube to his lungs bigger. I cried so much that I rusted myself on my nose which is in the centre of

Carpe Diem! On the 13th August, the new head, Mr William Hughes, introduced himself in assembly and told all the children the other head teacher had died. At the end of the day he called all the children into the hall and told them how nice the school was, and how nice the children were as well. That night was the start of the Blitz and I was so frightened, I could hear bombs dropping and heavy gun fire in the distance. The following day 300 children were absent. Their houses might have been bombed and they might have been killed. That afternoon the children who did turn up had an air raid practice.

On 3rd October 1940, I saw all the children rushing in and out for aid raids. One was at 10.40am and was all clear at 11.20am, and one at 11.30am and was all clear at 12.05pm. There was another air raid attack at 12.15pm and was all clear at 1.40pm. During the last raid the children were there for 1 hour 40 minutes. You can see how disrupting it was for everyone concerned....

The day I will remember most was 7th November 1945. Hitler committed suicide and the war was over! King George VI and Queen Elizabeth were going to go round all the cities so the school was closed.

GOODBYE AND FAREWELL

I know I moan a lot but it's quite good being a clock really. We've travelled through over 87 years now; I hope I haven't bored you to death. It's brought back fond memories for me.

I've seen lots of changes around me in Bournville. When I was first put up here I could see rolling green fields all around me. In the distance to my left I could see the new Cadbury factory, the recreation ground, railway sidings and a few of the first houses built by George Cadbury for his workers. Now, I'm afraid, it's changed beyond recognition. There are shops, a church, many more houses and a place called 'Cadbury World'. I think it's a sort of place where people go to find out about how chocolate is made and how the village of Bournville began. I hope my school is mentioned....

I often wonder what the future holds for me, will I still be here in another 87 years (2080 AD)? I hope you liked my story, do please come and see me, I will be pleased to see you. And remember CARPE DIEM, value every moment of the day, that applies just as much now as it did when George Cadbury had it built into my metal work.

	STATUTORY LISTING	YEAR	COMMENT
Bournville Junior School Linden Road Bournville	Grade II	1902-5	Designed by W Alexander Harvey.

THE FAMILY TREE AT NEW HALL, SUTTON COLDFIELD

BY ROBERT COOKE
WALMLEY JUNIOR SCOOL
SUTTON COLDFIELD

I watched the young seedling struggling to get out of the Earth thinking I'm not alone any longer. It reminded me of when I was growing out of the Earth and my mom was watching.

It all started one Friday morning when I was in the Earth and suddenly I started to get worried because all I could hear was a crash, bang, wallop. After it was quiet I popped my head out of the Earth and looked around in terror to see dead bodies and blood everywhere. I asked my mom what all the banging was for. She told me that the owner of the land, Edwin Earl of Mercia, he had a battle with William the Conqueror to try and win Edwin's land off him. William succeeded in winning Edwin's land and in 1071 Edwin was executed.

After the battle, life was quite boring. There was one time when it was winter and there was a bad hail storm. In 1226 a new owner Roger De Newburgh, the Earl of Warwick, was riding his horse and nearly trampled on me.

Then in 1455 there began another battle which history calls Wars of the Roses. The beautiful house built next to me and called New Hall by Sir John De Lizours in 1341 was owned by the King in 1487.

The person who owned it next was Thomas Gibbons in 1542. He was the first person to extend the house and I was worried that they might disturb my roots by digging the foundations.

Photo courtesy of Sutton Coldfield News.
Robert Cooke outside New Hall.

My favourite owner of the house was Henry Sacheverell who owned the house in 1590. His son Valens visited me often and collected acorns off the floor by me and he sometimes left one for me by my tree. So did Valens' son George. The sad bit was when George's chaplain Doctor Henry Sacheverell was imprisoned in New Hall because he was encouraging people to rebel. I sometimes felt sad because he spent hours looking out of the bars on his window.

The next owners of the house were the Chadwicks and my roots were again under threat in 1870 when more building work was done on the house.In 1885 New Hall became a boys boarding school. The best time was when the boys climbed my branches and made a tree house and played pirates in the tree house.

Some of the naughty boys crept out of the dormitory and threw their inkwells in the moat. The branches of my tree were used to cane them. They didn't half have a shock when they drained out the moat because they found hundreds of inkwells at the bottom of it. Some of the boys crept out at night and fished for the giant pike who was supposed to live in the moat. He wasn't very pleased when he got hit on the head by an inkwell.

In 1903 the next owner of the house was Walter Wilkinson. He had a blind wife who liked to ride around the land in her cart which was pulled by a donkey. Her husband had her name engraved on my trunk and she would spend many happy hours in the spring sitting under my branches.

The next owner of the house was Alfred Ernest Owen in 1923. His son loved fast cars and the forest became full of fumes and noise.

I'm really glad that the house has now become a hotel and I hope I will be able to live the rest of my life in peace.I wonder if this little sapling standing next to me will see as much change as I have.

New Hall by Emma Strange,aged 14,
Arthur Terry Secondary School,
Sutton Coldfield

	STATUTORY LISTING	YEAR	COMMENT
New Hall Walmley Road Sutton Coldfield	Grade I	13th or 14th Century	The oldest fully moated manor House in England

THE MOAT HOUSE
"HE'LL NEVER MAKE A GOOD ARCHITECT"

BY CLAUDIA DYER
COPPICE JUNIOR SCHOOL
SUTTON COLDFIELD

In 1672, Henry Pudsey, the town's richest man, died. His widow Jane Pudsey asked William Wilson to build a monument out of marble, to everyone's great surprise they fell in love and married. Jane's family disagreed bitterly, they called him common with little money. But Jane was proud of her new husband and persuaded King Charles II to make him a Knight, "Sir William Wilson", after he had built Moat House, Nottingham Castle and restored St Mary's Church following the fire in 1694. But Jane's family were still not convinced that he was just as good as them. When William Wilson died he wanted to be laid next to Jane, but the family refused.

Many, many years later, two girls called Joan and Sarah were walking on their way to the college but instead they went to have a look at Moat House, it was open to the public on Thursdays. They opened the door and stepped inside.

They looked around the house, when they were upstairs they looked in all the rooms. But there was one door that caught Joan's eye. She quickly grabbed Sarah and they listened at the door, they could hear the sound of voices. Then nothing....silence. Nervously, they pushed the door open....it was Jane and William Wilson's bedroom.

On the wall was a huge picture of William Wilson. By the picture was a marble fireplace and a wooden four-poster bed with silk drapes. And a wooden dressing table and some chairs and paintings. "Joan, can't we go now, the picture is giving me the creeps" Sarah muttered. "No, wait a minute" Joan shouted. "Anyway, what do you mean Sarah", "I feel as though I'm being followed" Sarah whispered. "Don't be stupid". "I don't like this building, it's horrible and William Wilson is so ugly". Suddenly a ray of light shone from the painting, and a ghostly figure stepped out. It was William Wilson. "You have insulted me" he bellowed. The girls froze scared and shaking. "You need to be there at that time to understand how hard it was".

BACK IN TIME

He held out his hands to them and they could feel themselves being pulled into and beyond the painting. "I will take you back in time to show you how hard it was to build Moat House". "But we can't go, we haven't got time". "Time will not move while you're with me". So Joan and Sarah stepped into the painting, they were swirling round and round in a mass of colours.

THE MOAT HOUSE

The Moat House by Jon Parsons, Coppice Junior School

"We're here" said William, "look at all my men building it". "Over there is my wife Jane and her family" said William. Joan and Sarah saw them talking. "They despise me, whatever I do is not good enough, that is why I'm building Moat House" William said. "Why don't they like you?" the girl protested. William was silent, then he muttered "because they think I'm common". "They have seen the plans for the house and they think it's poor craftsmanship". "Jane is proud of me and is persuading King Charles to give me a Knighthood" William said. "Go and listen for yourselves". Joan and Sarah muttered to each other and wandered over to them but kept a fair distance away.

"I don't know what you have to be proud of daughter, he's common and he'll never make a good architect" her father said. "Well father, I think Moat House looks beautiful" said Jane. "Child, you're foolish, common and noble don't mix". "But father, William isn't common" said Jane. "He would not be so common if he were doing something useful like transport" said Jane's father.

"Father, don't talk about my husband like that, he's just as good as we are. Anyway, I've asked King Charles to give him a Knighthood" Jane said in a flutter. "You did

what girl, you don't know what you're saying, he doesn't deserve a Knighthood, he's common. I demand that you write a letter to King Charles saying that you have changed your mind" her father bellowed. "Father, why tell me to do such a thing" Jane protested. "The plans are worthless, the house will look terrible, and who will live in it, it's all very well him building the house to impress us, but we've already got a house" Jane's father shouted. "We will live in it father" said Jane. Joan and Sarah walked back to William Wilson. "We're sorry, we didn't know how hard it was for you" said the girls. "Hold on tight, it won't take long" said William.

Joan, Sarah and William Wilson went back through the swirls of colours and landed back in the room, it was the same time as when they had gone. "I'm tired" said Sarah. "Farewell, I hope you understand now" said William. "Thank you, we're very sorry for what we said, we thought the house was beautiful" the girls chanted. Suddenly the light drew back in, and the thin wispy voice of William Wilson faded and he was gone. "Let's go Sarah, I wonder what today will be". "Yes, I wonder".

	STATUTORY LISTING	YEAR	COMMENT
Moat House Lichfield Road Sutton Coldfield	Grade II*	Circa 1680	Architect - Sir William Wilson

A Factual Study of Warren House Farm

BY CLASS 6
TOPCLIFFE J.I. SCHOOL
CASTLE VALE

Warren House Farm by Trevor Evans

Warren House Farm is situated half a mile north of Walmley on Walmley Road (B4148). We've been told that Warren House Farm got its name because there were supposed to be rabbit warrens there. It is interesting that there are only a few Artesian ditches in the country and one of these is supposed to be behind the farm.

Warren House Farm was built around the year 1530 by Bishop Vesey. Bishop Vesey was born in Sutton Coldfield in 1462 and died in 1555. He was a very generous man who wanted to make life better for the people who lived in the Sutton Coldfield area.

Bishop Vesey built fifty-one stone houses but only seven are still lived in. Every one of the houses were built in the same way. They were all built of sandstone and each one of them had a spiral staircase, which was built around an upright column called a newel post. Spiral staircases were popular at this time because they took up less room and were cheaper to build.

The house is very solid and is built of large blocks of red sandstone. As sandstone is mined in this area the stone is probably local stone. The walls are about 60cm thick and they are now covered over with rough-cast. The sandstone can still be seen by the side of the fireplace. The large downstairs room has a brick pillar sticking out of the wall. You can tell the bricks are handmade because they have a diagonal line in them. They are held together with mortar and you can still see the horse hair which was mixed in with the mortar. On the south side there is a chimney stack which sticks out and on this is a red sandstone buttress.

Warren House Farm by Anthony Shanahan

Recent extension

West facing

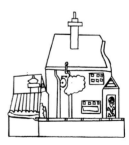

The house has lots of very, very old oak beams and some of them have had strengtheners fastened to them. An extension was added to the existing building about a hundred years after the house was built and a plaque with 1671 on it can be

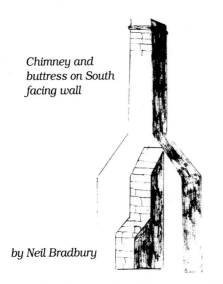

Chimney and buttress on South facing wall

by Neil Bradbury

seen in the brickwork of this part of the building.

Upstairs was a granary that you could only get to through a trap door. This was to stop rats and mice getting into the sacks of grain. There was a vertical ladder for people to climb up through the trap door into the granary. The granary had three window slits for the light to come through. The slits didn't have any glass in them. One source suggested that they were arrow slits.

When we looked for information about houses we found that in 1530 wealthy people lived in mansions and poor people lived in timber framed houses. So we think that people living at Warren House Farm were somewhere between the two. Not long after the farm was built a footpath linked it with the ford keeper's cottage in Wylde Green Road and this was also a Vesey house. There was a trackway to Newhall Mill and the grain grown at Warren House Farm was probably taken there to be

ground. We thought about the changes to the farm over the years and decided that it would have had a thatched roof. Tiles were added later. Its main use was as a farm but then by Victorian times it had become a family home. This is shown on the details when it was sold in 1881.

A pump was put in the yard around this time but it is no longer there. More recently a modern staircase, central heating and a conservatory have been added. Over the years the steps of the spiral staircase have worn away and have been levelled off with concrete then tiled.

Although it is mainly a family home it still has a link with farming because the people who live there keep hens and ducks and there are stables for horses.

By Matthew Owens

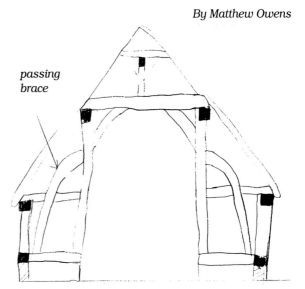

passing brace

These are like the beams in the attic. They are crown - post type with a passing brace to give support

This shows how the beams were fastened together

by Neil Bradbury

STATUTORY LISTING	YEAR	COMMENT
Warren House Farmhouse Grade II Walmley Sutton Coldfield	Early 16th Century	One of the houses built by Bishop Vesey

39

WATER ORTON BRIDGE

BY ANDREW MALIN
WALMLEY JUNIOR SCHOOL
SUTTON COLDFIELD

Andrew Malin

Water Orton Bridge

It was a fine evening in July as I was alerted to the rumbling of carriage wheels approaching. I stood up hold armfuls of sweetly scented tulips, roses, and carnation to tempt the travellers to buy my flowers. The coaches and carriages were forced to slow down as they approached the bridge and there I waited hoping to earn a few pennies.

This carriage did not slow down though, it tore along and clattered onto the bridge. It was lucky to remain on all four wheels as it swayed from side to side. The driver realised too late that someone was in his path.

Peter Pikeman had served his country and was injured during one of the battles. He had been left with an permanent limp, and he was often seen on the bridge returning from the Beggars Bush Inn, a little bit drunk!

On this night he staggered and limped, and you should have seen the expression on his face when he saw the coach bearing down on him.

He jumped out of the way but was unable to keep his balance and fell over the wall. His fingers gripped the top of the bridge wall but he could not hold on. He dropped like a sack of stones and landed with a SPLASH!!!

The coach stopped and they all tried unsuccessfully to reach poor Peter Pikeman.

It is said that to this day he can still be seen trying to climb the wall to Water Orton Bridge.

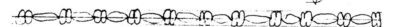

Radar & The Chamberlain Tower
By Alexander Smith, Age 6
Hallfield School, Edgbaston

Warren House Farm by Trevor Evans, Topcliffe J.I. School, Castle Vale

By Samina, Arden Primary School

The Old Rectory by Vahjad, Brays School, Sheldon

The Old Rectory by class one, Brays School, Sheldon

St Giles Church by Senior Class One, Brays School, Sheldon

KEY STAGE 3- HISTORY

The use of historical sources, including buildings and sites, continues to run as a thread through Key Stage 3. Pupils are also required to investigate topics, to organise and communicate historical knowledge and understanding in a variety of ways. No local history is specifically required at Key Stage 3,although using the local area to exemplify national history is an element of best practice. However there are many opportunities through the Key Stage to add a local perspective and so enhance learning.

The study of architecture is prescribed in four out of the five Core Study Units. The legacy of Roman Britain, of Medieval Britain, of Tudor and Stuart times and of the eighteenth and nineteenth centuries can be seen in many local areas today. Each period has left a legacy through its architecture which has influenced and inspired later generations.

The study of a building, even a relatively humble one, will illustrate wider historical significance.

It is through the higher levels of history Attainment Targets that pupils have opportunities to develop and demonstrate their knowledge,understanding and skills. In particular they should

- Investigate different kinds of change (AT1)

- distinguish between features of past societies which change and those which remain constant (AT1)

- examine different kinds of cause and consequence (AT1)

- Study ideas, beliefs and attitudes of people (AT1)

- develop an understanding that interpretations of the past can be conveyed in different ways, through a variety of media (AT2)

- consider reasons why interpretations of the past differ (AT2)

- study a range of historical sources and comment on their value, including the use of buildings and sites (AT3)

Even at Key Stage 3 stories are useful for helping pupils to understand why events took place and for helping them to develop historical skills.

Stories can help pupils to understand why people in the past acted as they did and also that other decisions could have been made, that there could have been other outcomes and that people often hold very different points of view. Stories are a very important element in learning about the past and one too often ignored with older pupils.

Erica Pounce
History Advisory Teacher

Reference: History in the National Curriculum DES 1991

A Queen's visit to Kings Norton

By Angela Weston
Teacher
Turves Green Girls School,
Northfield

The Saracens Head, King's Norton

Birmingham can tell us many tales of the past, particularly those involving the English Civil War, and great battles between Charles I's Cavaliers and the Roundheads of Parliament. During this time the towns of Warwick and Worcester fought on opposite sides - Warwick being Parliamentary and Worcester being Royalist.

Parliamentary and Roundhead armies often turned owners out of houses, in order for the army to be garrisoned in the buildings. These houses were often in key areas for defence reasons.The following concerns the Saracen's Head at King's Norton, Birmingham, which lies within the parish of the old medieval church of St. Nicholas, once in the parish of Moseley.

The Saracen's Head a half-timbered 15th Century building was owned by the King's

Bailiff or Sheriff, and for such a person only a building as fine as the Saracen's Head was good enough.

Our story begins with a brave young lady who became Queen Henrietta Maria . The year is 1623.

"I was the daughter of the King of France and only 14 years old when I first saw Charles I the King of England. I immediately fell in love with him. Two years later at the age of 16 I became his wife. As part of my wedding gift, I was given the village of Kings Norton.

At this time many people from all over the country were sailing to North America and settling there. They called these settlements 'colonies' and one of them was named Maryland after me.

When Civil War broke out I went to Holland. There I sold the crown jewels to buy arms and ammunition. With the help of Dutch officers, I wanted to fight for the king, my husband, who I loved very much. In a ship loaded with weapons, I landed at Bridlington in Yorkshire. The navy supported Parliament and tried to stop me from landing. That night they fired their guns at the house where I was sleeping. I managed to save my life by running from the house in bare feet.

However I was determined to take the weapons to the King who was waiting for me in Oxford. I marched South and on my way

I called at King's Norton - a town which had seen many skirmishes, and seen many of its men killed or wounded.

By the time I arrived in King's Norton the year was 1643 and I had gathered a huge army of 6,000 men. That night they camped around the village , some were cavalry men, others were highly trained artillery men on foot - but whoever or whatever their post, the purpose was to protect me, their Queen. The chattering and ringing around the camp fire went on all night, but I slept peacefully at the Saracen's Head, the home of my bailiff.

The following day we moved on towards Oxford taking with us the ammunition and soldiers which were so important to the King. The rest of my journey is another story."

There is still a room at the Saracen's Head known as the Queen's Room, where Henrietta Maria spent the night.

THE COMING OF QUEEN HENRIETTA MARIA TO KING'S NORTON

Fair and fierce, fierce and fair
She rides as a Queen that chides despair

Gallants bold, full thousands three,
Hers by their stout hearts' fealty.

True and fast, fast and true,
Rides as men whom the gods endue.

Ride apace, the Queen ahead
"God and King" doth cry adread.

"Haste, haste, and on and on,
Or never the kingly cause be won"

Sets the sun o'er Norton crest
Stay they all at the Queen's behest.

At the House of God, a whirling flame
The swords flash high at the Royal name.

Shout! O Village of Norton, Shout!
Old and young in a joyous rout.

Peal the bells in loyalty
To the peerless Queen and her gallantrie.

Sleep, O Queen, in the ancient place,
Sleep an thou mayest, by God's good grace.

Queen adread; Queen fair to see,
The vigil of prayer is lain on thee

In the summer night o'er the curtained sky
Thou seest the sentinel stars stride by.

Thou watchest them all in their courses nod,
O'er the House of God, o'er the House of God.

On, on! They bid thee on;
Summon thy gallants, and get thee gone

To thy King at need. It yet may be
Thy foes shall kneel to the King and thee.

Sleep, O village of Norton, sleep!
'Ere ever the rays of morning leap

At the eastern gates, afar, afar,
The Queen rides under the morning star.

E M Rudland: Ballads of Old Birmingham

St. Laurence's Church, Northfield

THE STUART MAIL
ST. LAURENCE'S CHURCH
IN THE CIVIL WAR ERA

BY RADMILA TOPALOVIC
TURVES GREEN GIRLS' SCHOOL
NORTHFIELD

Last Sunday, many Christians went to St. Laurence church. The 600 year old church was packed with many people, probably praying that this war would finally stop.

Worcester, the Royalist side are fighting against Warwick, the Parliament side. The church is probably the only building which is not garrisoned by soldiers. Lots of buildings have been occupied by fierce garrisons and many people do not like it, especially when they are turned out.

The Church provided shelter for poor, humble christians and is holding out against this battle quite well. The church was first built around the 11th century along with Great Stone Inn and the village pound. Northfield, a small village owned by Kings Norton is doing quite well but there is still the fear of being attacked by soldiers.

I spoke to the vicar of St. Laurence church and he is very worried about what will happen to his fellow people. He is on nobody's side and just cares about the people around the area. He says he just hopes this silly battle will soon stop and cause no further serious trouble.

Meanwhile, 2 big houses quite nearby, next to Frankley Beeches and Turves Green have been garrisoned. The names of the houses are Hawkesley House and Frankley Lodge. The Middlemore family are very annoyed about being turned out of their home, Hawkesley House. Lets just hope that the soldiers will leave small Northfield alone and their special church - St. Laurence.

Reported by Radmila Topalovic

St. Laurence Church is open every Sunday early in the morning and there is an afternoon service as well.

	STATUTORY LISTING	YEAR	COMMENT
Church of St. Laurence Church Hill, Northfield	Grade I	From 12th Century	Designed by GF Bodley

48

*Aidan Travers at the Hovel,
Jerrys Lane, Erdington*

THE HOVEL
JERRYS LANE, ERDINGTON

BY *AIDAN TRAVERS*
PERRY COMMON SECONDARY
SCHOOL, ERDINGTON

Joe was nearly six years old when his father said they were moving to another cottage because it had more land. He wondered who he would have to play with when he wasn't at school, he had two sisters, but sisters aren't very good to play with, are they?

When he saw the cottage his father and mother had bought, he loved it. It had such a big garden with a beautiful hedge all around it, with lots and lots of different birds flying around. He even saw a squirrel running away and he said "I'll bet there's other animals as well".

He was usually lonely while his father and sometimes his mother were working in the fields around, growing extra plants and flowers to sell, because you see his father had a stall in the market called the 'Bull Ring' in the town.

One day he had a lovely surprise, his mother told him a little boy called Jimmy was coming to play with him. This made him happy as they would have lots of adventures together and they did. They watched the birds building their nests, they climbed the trees, played hide and seek, had a go on the swing his dad had made and when they were tired of these they decided to explore. You see, with the garden being so big they had never been to the bottom of it. It was so different, it had lovely trees, a little pond with tadpoles and fish in it and a little stream, but the biggest surprise of all when they went further on into the corner was a little house, such a

wee house. "Did anyone live in it?" they asked one another, "someone must have, look there was a gate leading into Jerrys Lane", but it was locked. When they tried the door of the little house it opened and they went in! Oh, it was so small, only two tiny rooms, one to live in and a kitchen. A staircase went up to two small bedrooms. "Only room for a bed" said Jimmy "and look at the tiny windows" said Joe, "I shall have to ask my Dad who it belongs to".

When his Dad came home he said it belonged to them and yes people did live in it, in fact Joe's Grandma was coming to live in it. Joe and Jimmy were so interested they asked how it came to be there, Joe's Dad told him it was built a long time ago, in about 1740, one hundred years before the cottage they were living in was built. Two brothers by the name of Biddle built it without permission and the Lord of the Manor who the land belonged to, was cross, but allowed them to keep it for 6 pence rent a week. Its proper name was a 'Hovel' and because it is so very old and unusual he asked Joe if he would always keep it when he grew up, and look after the cottage they lived in. Joe agreed to this and kept his promise.

From then on Joe and Jimmy played many other games and had several different adventures in the 'Hovel', even when his Grandma came, but that's another story.

	STATUTORY LISTING	YEAR	COMMENT
The Hovel, Jerrys Lane Erdington	Grade II	Circa 1800	Farm labourers Cottage

HARBORNE HALL
-A GLIMPSE INTO THE PAST

BY HEATHER O'MALLEY
KING EDWARD VI
CAMP HILL SCHOOL FOR GIRLS
KINGS HEATH

My story is set fifty years ago, near to the start of the Second World War. The setting is the historic Harborne Hall, which at that time was a convent.

The coach pulled up alongside the pretty Georgian house in the centre of Harborne. Madelaine, alighting from the coach, thought that the house looked wonderful. Its walls were white and sparkling, and the gardens a delight; you could almost smell the mystery in the air. Her guess was that the house had seen many years, and witnessed many events. If the walls could talk.....she was sure they would have a lot to say. Many people had remarked that Madelaine was better acquainted with the clouds than the real world! In some ways, the girl reflected, this was true, but it didn't mean she was just a dreamer.

As the class trailed into the house, Madelaine was struck by the elaborate panelling that decorated the walls, and its feeling of antiquity. Someone in the school group laughed, and muttered "Daydreaming...!". Madelaine turned away, blushing furiously. She had not meant to make her thoughts so obvious. Looking closely at the dark red panelling, she began to sense a story unfolding, and very soon a legend ran before her eyes, as clearly as the printed page.....

The rising bell rang sharply in Sister Emmanuelles' ears. It was time to get up for morning prayers and breakfast. Christmas was fast approaching, and there were still many toys to be made for the children of Harborne village. It was the year 1938, and

there was talk of another war with Germany. No-one believed it, of course, England was still recovering from the 1914-18 war, and another conflict between the countries might be disastrous. Sister Emmanuelle looked out on to the placid grounds of Harborne Hall. The sun was just rising; a golden ball encased in blossom-pink clouds. After the usual breakfast of bread and butter, Sister Emmanuelle departed to the sewing room to make tiny toys and trinkets for the children of Harborne. This took her up to Angelica, where she prayed for peace in England. She was one of the oldest nuns in the convent, well past the age of seventy-five, but "still going strong". She had devoted herself to God and Harborne Hall. It seemed such a long time since she had left her home in Brittany, some thirty years before, with seven other nuns. She had been there ever since, and now thought of Harborne Hall as her home.....

Madelaine blinked and, as her eyes closed, time moved on again, and although the story was becoming harder to follow, she could just make out.....

.....Sister Emmanuelle skipping merrily in time to the music of the childrens' Christmas party. She hadn't a care in the world, and all thoughts of war had been banished from her mind.....

50

Madelaine turned away, tears in her eyes. If only Sister Emmanuelle knew what was to come; the war she feared, suffering, loss and death. A far more thoughtful and serious girl left Harborne Hall that day. She had been right; the Hall did have a wonderful history. She had only been allowed a glimpse into the past, but for Madelaine history had come alive on that day.

Harborne Hall 1914 - 1918
Photo courtesy of GEC Avery Historical Museum

Sources: 1 *A History of Harborne Hall by Frances Wilmot*

2 *Personal visits to Harborne Hall for information. Many thanks to the staff of the Hall for making my research possible and enjoyable.*

Harborne Hall today

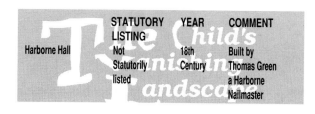

	STATUTORY LISTING	YEAR	COMMENT
Harborne Hall	Not Statutorily listed	18th Century	Built by Thomas Green a Harborne Nailmaster

THE LLOYD FAMILY

YEAR II
BY GOLDEN HILLOCK SCHOOL
SMALL HEATH

The Lloyd's House

INTRODUCTION

Sampson Lloyd had an Iron Making business in Dale End - near Digbeth, Birmingham. At that time Birmingham was much smaller. The area of Sparkbrook was open countryside.

He moved to Birmingham from Wales in 1695.

He had a large house built on what is now Farm Park. There was farm land all around it. There were some farm buildings (now broken down) and later a church (called Christ Church).

He could travel easily from his new home to his Iron Works, it would only take him about ten minutes.

Sampson Lloyd moved into his new house in 1722. His new house was very large. It had many big windows to let in light and lots of chimneys, as each room had a fire place. The servants would live on the top floor.

In 1725 Sampson died and left his business to his sons Charles and Sampson .

OUR VISIT TO A LISTED BUILDING IN SPARKBROOK

On 15th March 1993, our group, which is a history group, went to visit the Lloyd building with Mr Whitehouse and Mr Binnie. The building is very old and broken, although some parts have been repaired.

52

The Lloyd house was built by Sampson Lloyd around 300 years ago. Sampson Lloyd was a very rich man who came to Birmingham from Wales.

LLOYD FAMILY HISTORY

In 1964 Mr Humphrey Lloyd began to gather all the information he could find in the family history. He wrote to all his relations and they told him all he knew.He collected together family letters, diaries and account books, some of them were nearly 300 years old. He found many old drawings and photographs of members of the family. He visited libraries in London to fit the pieces of information together, like a jig-saw puzzle. After that he wrote the story of his family. This gave us lots of information about the Lloyd family.

LOOKING BACK

In 1778 Sampson Lloyd II set up a bank with his friend John Taylor, it was called Taylor and Lloyds bank. He was quite an old man. His eldest son, Sampson, did most of the work in the bank, with the help of his second son, Charles. Charles was a very good banker.

The Bank opened for business on 3rd June 1765 at a house belonging to John Taylor in Dale End. Soon the bank was very busy. In the room nearest to the street sat two clerks, behind tall desks, who took the money and bills and wrote it all down. Sampson knew that most of the banks were in London and although there were many busy merchants in Birmingham, there was no bank.

After about five years the Lloyds decided that the time had come to start a London branch. Both of the banks grew steadily, even in bad times. The people trusted the Lloyds.

Sampson would often go for a walk about Birmingham. As he did so, he would notice the many changes that had taken place in his life time and many of the new things which he and his family had helped to bring about, then he would return to his grand, new house.

Lloyd House in Farm Park

Source: The Lloyds, Family History Patches, Marie Rowlands Nelson

	STATUTORY LISTING	YEAR	COMMENT
Lloyd House Sampson Road Sparkhill	Grade II*	Mid 18th Century	Built by Sampson LLoyd II

NATIONAL CURRICULUM HISTORY IN SPECIAL SCHOOLS

Pupils in most Special schools are being given the opportunities to study National Curriculum History. Pupils work on this historical content in the Programme of Study within the appropriate Key Stage but pupils tackle Attainment Targets at the levels which are relevant to them.

For most special school pupils direct experience is often the most relevant way of learning and visits to local sites and buildings combined with living history activities are particularly successful.

Stories of course are essential for bringing history to life. Stories are also useful in special schools for reinforcing basic skills such as sequencing, understanding why events happen, using common words and phrases relating to the passing of time, reinforcing language work and for helping pupils to communicate their awareness and understanding of history.

Erica Pounce
History Advisory Teacher
Curriculum Support Service

Selly Manor by Dexter Brown, Year 7, Selly Oak School

	STATUTORY LISTING	YEAR	COMMENT
Selly Manor Sycamore Road Bournville	Grade II	14th - 16th Century	Bought by George Cadbury in 1907

THE OLD RECTORY, SHELDON

BY *SENIOR CLASS ONE*
BRAYS SCHOOL, SHELDON

"The story is based on the Old Rectory in Sheldon and is about the life and times of Thomas Bray.

Thomas Bray is of particular importance to us as our school is named after him.

The Old Rectory now lies in the middle of Sheldon Country Park.

Thank you to Sheldon Library, Central Birmingham Library, Steve Nelson, Sheldon Country Park, who have all assisted us with our story.

Our story begins at the Old Rectory, Sheldon.

OLD RECTORY FARM

This is an historic building which dates back to the 17th Century. From 1690-1729 it was home to Dr Thomas Bray, Rector of St Giles Church and founder of the Society for the Promotion of Christian Knowledge. His contribution to the church is commemorated in the names of Brays Road and Brays Special School.

The farm buildings were added during the 19th Century when the site was developed as a farm.

WHO WAS THOMAS BRAY?

Thomas Bray was born in Morton, Shropshire, and was educated at Oswestry School and then went to Oxford. After taking holy orders, he became Rector of St Giles Church, Sheldon, in 1690. It was from here that Thomas Bray wrote his books and from where he set forth on his journeys to America.

Sheldon in 1680 was a country parish and there were about 500 people living in the area. Sheldon today is very different. There are about 40,000 people living in the area. Modern housing, a shopping centre and the busy Coventry Road have helped to change Sheldon from a quiet country village to a bustling town.

It is very different to life in Thomas Bray's time.

When Thomas Bray had finished writing his first religious book it sold many copies and Bray became popular.

The Bishop of London, Henry Compton, got to hear of Bray and asked him if he would go to Maryland, USA, to help to spread the Christian word. Bray decided that to help the missionaries in America it would be a

good idea to have a library. Bray decided that parochial libraries should be set up. In 1698 there were very few books and the missionaries were too poor to buy them. Bray was so pleased with the libraries he decided that the idea should spread to other countries and that other authors should also donate books.

Dr Bray set up 16 libraries in Maryland. The chief library was at Annapolis. It had 1,000 books and cost £400. It was the first lending library in America. Bray used his own money to help pay for books for the ministers in America. Dr Bray spent a lot of time in Maryland and on his return he founded the Society for the Propagation of the Gospel in foreign parts.

Bray continued to write religious books to help pay for the setting up of the libraries. The libraries were so successful in America that he decided they should be in every Deanery throughout England. For a small subscription people would be given the chance to borrow books. Not only religious books, but history, geography and travel.

In 1697 Thomas Bray formed the Society for the Propogation of Christian Knowledge and he gave a large sum of money to help establish it. This was to be the Church's oldest missionary and is still going strong today.

Thomas Bray spent a lot of time travelling between England and America.

Thomas Bray was a teacher and he devised a system of graded teaching to suit the age of the pupils.

1st - up to 9 years

2nd - 9-13 years

3rd - youth

Each group was given lessons according to their ability.

Bray had his scheme printed for use in America.

In his lifetime Thomas Bray did many things:-

1. He formed two religious societies.

2. He helped to form church schools for the children of the poor.

3. He involved himself in looking at prison reform.

4. He formed a library system for the church throughout the world.

Drawn by Musarat Bibi

In January 1730 Dr Bray became seriously ill and on 15 February he died.

In his Will Dr Bray left a library of books for the "use of the Rector of Sheldon forever". The books are now so valuable that they are in Birmingham Central Library for safekeeping.

	STATUTORY LISTING	YEAR	COMMENT
Old Rectory Church Road Sheldon	Grade II	18th Century in appearence	Thomas Bray lived here from 1690 - 1729

A Day in the life of Richard Smalbroke

BY YEAR 5
PINES SCHOOL
HODGE HILL

Blakesley Hall

When I get up I get out of my bed. My bed is a big bed made of wood with ropes to hold the mattress. You can take my bed to pieces by pulling out the pegs. I share my bed with 6 of my brothers.

We wear nightshirts in bed. We get up and push the bed back under, there is a separate bed that fits underneath. We have a jug of water to wash with and we clean our teeth with ash and chalk.

We all go downstairs to the great parlour for our breakfast. We have toast, 2 pieces made with the bread that the servants make. All of us boys have to go to school to learn how to write and we use a quill and ink to write with. The girls stay at home to knit and sew.

After school, we go to the long gallery to play skittles and pea shooters.

For dinner we have chicken, peas, potatoes, roast parsnips, carrots and egg and cheese and apple. We help ourselves from the servants.

We take exercise by walking down the Long Gallery and then it is bed-time when we blow out our candles and rush lights.

Information from:-

Blakesley Hall Visit and Visitors Book

Worksheets

Ginn 'Tudors and Stuarts'

Selection of Library Books

Note: This work followed a visit to Blakesley Hall. Birmingham. Schools can arrange a visit with the Schools Liaison Teacher at Blakesley Hall. Tel: 021 789 7027

	STATUTORY LISTING	YEAR	COMMENT
Blakesley Hall Blakesley Road Yardley	Grade II*	16th Century	Timber framed farmhouse built by Richard Smallbroke

SOME KINGFISHERS FIND OUT ABOUT THEN & NOW

BY MARK, KEITH, JOHN, RICHARD, GARY, NICHOLAS AND PETER & THEIR TEACHERS SUE NEVILLE & SUE BEASLEY BRIDGE SCHOOL ERDINGTON

Lindens 1993 Sue Neville with pupils

LINDENS
Reservoir Road, Erdington

Now it is Social Services Offices but it was a children's home. Teacher, Sue Neville, worked at Lindens as a student in 1967.

CHILDREN LIVED THERE THEN

This photo was taken 26 years ago. Has Sue changed? "We found the same step". "What has changed?" "What looks the same?"

"What's his name?'" asks Nicholas, pointing to the boy in the photo. "I can't remember ", admits Sue. "It was a long time ago."

We have been doing a project on the theme of changes. We've observed many changes near to our own school in Reservoir Road, Erdington. We visited the former 'Gardens' area and made a video at the building site.

The Kingfisher Group (9-10 years old) made a more detailed study of one of the buildings, the Lindens, and enjoyed finding out how its use has changed over the years. The 'old' photos were a good starting point. We could look at them carefully, talk about them and try to work out problems by looking for details in the photos. Then we explored the building, met people and questioned them and generally became more aware of our local environment.

Lindens 1967 Sue Neville with pupils

58

Lindens 1993

We found this building too. It was a church...but it's changing now.

Gary finds the name on the building. "Why did the big house need a chimney?"
"Because of the fire. They got rid of it"
"Gas fire now", says John.

Church 1967

Church 1993

All photos courtesy of Bridge School

LINDENS NOW

We made an appointment to look inside the Lindens.

"The people work there now because the telephones are ringing!" says Gary.
"The stairs look just the same", says Sue
..."and this door".
"No beds up here now. But this is fun. I can phone downstairs."

We found a new building next to the old and looked at the differences.

Next we go to Erdington Library to find out that Lindens was built about 1898. That's nearly 100 years old!

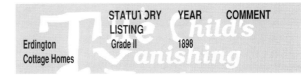

	STATUTORY LISTING	YEAR	COMMENT
Erdington Cottage Homes	Grade II	1898	

59

This book is sponsored by

Barclays Bank

Birmingham Education Business Partnership

Birmingham Training and Enterprise Council

Brewin Books

Dillons The Bookstore

Laing's Charitable Trust

Maxim Construction Limited

S T Walker and Partners

Young Historian Scheme

Wayland Publishers

Midland Bank 1920's
Photo courtesy of Dillons The Bookstore

THE FIRST DAY
(128 NEW STREET)

I approached the arched entrance of the bank flanked either side by huge granite columns. The sound of my heart thumping in my ears almost equalled the sound of the huge brass knocker as I pounded on the walnut doors.

"Yer'll be alright, yer'll soon settle in" my mother had said as she kissed me goodbye and thrust my wrapped bread and dripping lunch into my hands at 7.00 a.m. that morning. Not having the tram fare, I had walked the distance from our back to back house in Floodgate Street to New Street. No. 128 was spanking new and had brought applause for the architect, Edward Holmes.

If it had not been my mother's persistent encouragement for me to learn to read and write and my uncle's "connections" I would not be here today.

The huge doors were opened by a bearded well dressed man with a monocle. "Ah you must be the new lad. Come this way" he said. My footsteps echoed on the black and white chequered marble tiles as I gazed in awe at the splendid banking hall.

A thousand lights struck the marble and bounced back to the huge cast iron domed ceiling with its myriad panes of coloured etched glass.

As we entered the bank manager's office, I looked around at the wood panelled walls, the fire burning cosily in the hearth and the rows and rows of books and thought to myself, "one day..."

Note: **DILLONS THE BOOKSTORE** *moved to the former Midland Bank building at 128 New Street in August 1993. The historic building developed for Dillons by Hortons Estates Limited was completely restored. The Grade II listed building dates back to 1869 when it was the home of the Birmingham Midland Bank. Special facilities in the new bookstore include a Reading Room and a Teacher/Librarian Resource Centre with a reference area for bibliographic research. There is also a major Children's Department with special features. Special thanks go to Dillons the Bookstore for sponsorship of the publication of this book.*

by Sue Cooke
Planning & Architecture
Birmingham City Council

	STATUTORY LISTING	YEAR	COMMENT
128 New Street Birmingham City Centre	Grade II	1867 - 1869	Designed by Edward Holmes

DILLONS
THE BOOKSTORE

VICTORIA'S RETRIBUTION

I'd like to tell you a story, a story about what happened long ago to naughty children.

It all began even before your parents were born. On the 21 July 1891, the Prince and Princess of Wales opened the New Victoria Law Courts, described in the News of the Day, as the finest modern building in the country. I had been chosen to report on the first Assize held just nine days after the opening of the new building. My heart was beating rapidly as with excitement I stepped into the huge unwelcoming hall. Sunlight streamed through stained glass windows one of which depicted Her Majesty Queen Victoria in 1837, the year she ascended the throne. I made some notes in my shorthand notebook. This would make interesting news for readers of the Birmingham Gazette. I was in plenty of time so I wandered around the hall reading the verses and sayings, etched into the walls.

I walked through a mass of terracotta corridors to Court No. 6 and took my place in the section reserved for the press.

The first case approached the bench. This involved two 12 year old boys accused of pickpocketing. Their dirty faces looked so pitiable. They stood hands shoved in over-large trousers rolled up at the ankle and secured by a belt at the waist. Their grim faced mothers accompanied them. The magistrate peered at the boys through the pince-nez perched on the end of his nose and asked the mothers for an explanation.

"His father's already kicked seven kettles out of him yer worship for bringing shame on a respectable household" said one. "Anyway it's t'other that led him to bad ways" she said, pointing a boney finger at the other boy.

That started an argument between the two women. The Magistrate's voice boomed out "Stop this disgraceful bickering. Do you have no respect? This is a Court of Law." He then asked the other woman for an explanation of her son's behaviour. Upon hearing that the boy was becoming uncontrollable and had no father, he announced his judgement. "I order that this boy receives 6 strokes of the birch, the other's father having already meted out retribution and in future keep your children under control. Next case".

I watched horrified as the mothers smiled at such a violent sentence. Probably with relief that they hadn't had to pay a fine. Judging by their clothes, moth eaten bonnets and men's boots, the Court would have been lucky to have collected any financial compensation.

And so continued the first Assize at Birmingham's Victoria Law Courts.

By Sue Cooke
Planning & Architecture
Birmingham City Council

Note: The characters in this story are fictitious but cases of a similar nature were heard in the 19th Century Law Courts.

The Victoria Law Courts have recently been refurbished with the work carried out by **MAXIM CONSTRUCTION OF NORTHFIELD.** *The Law Courts rebuilding is an example of just one of their restoration projects in their programme of concern for the built environment which has led them to generously sponsor the publication of this book.*

Court No. 5, The Hanging Court, Victoria Law Courts, Corporation Street

	STATUTORY LISTING	YEAR	COMMENT
Victoria Law Courts Corporation Street	Grade I	1887 - 91	Design won in competition by Sir Aston Webb & Ingress Bell

maxim

Maxim Construction Limited

LIVING IN A FLOODGATE STREET BACK-TO-BACK

BY DR. CARL CHINN
COMMUNITY HISTORIAN
THE UNIVERSITY OF BIRMINGHAM

Photo courtesy of Ivy M. Caswell.
Infant Welfare Centre, Medical Mission Floodgate Street. Early 1900's
Ivy's mother was one of the voluntary helpers who started the centre.

BILLY'S STORY

The other day, after school we 'ad some dead posh ladies come up our street. They were wearing frocks which were ever s' nice and they had big 'ats on, with lots of feathers. One of the ladies stopped our wench and 'er asked 'er summat. Our Pem dayn answer 'er 'cus 'er dayn know what t' say. I was playin' tipcat with me mates and our Pem called me over.

'Billy!' 'er said, 'Come 'ere! These ladies wan' summat!' So I wen' over.

'Young man' this one lady said and 'er said it like 'er 'ad a gob-stopper in 'er mouth, 'Where is your mother? Why are you all playing in the street like so many street urchins? Why are you not indoors doing your homework?'

'Er threw that many questions at me, I dayn know which one to catch first. It was like bein' at school. I tried to answer 'er but me tongue seemed to get bigger, s' big that I couldn't seem to move it. Any road up. I gorrit out that our Mom was in the house collaring. An' I pointed t' where our 'ouse was, 2 back of 59, Floodgate Street.

THE LADY'S STORY

My friend and I all live in Edgbaston. Recently we listened to a slum vicar telling us about the terrible poverty in the central wards of Birmingham, about the lack of decency amongst many of the people, about the need for ladies like us to go into the slums and to raise up the poor. So we have come to Floodgate Street. We have been told that it is an area where the people need the advice of those like us who are better educated.

It is so drab and dirty here. It is so unlike Edgbaston. There are no trees, there is no grass, there is no space. No birds singing and you cannot see the sky for the smoke billowing forth from the surrounding factories. It is a horrid, mean, squalid place.

The children are running about with no supervision. No wonder they have no morals. Where are their mothers? I shall ask one of these urchins for his mother and I shall remonstrate with her at her lack of attention to her children.

THE MOM'S STORY

I'd bin carding buttons all day. I was whacked out. The kids'd come 'um and all I'd got to gie 'em was a piece with dripping on. I 'ad to send 'em out to eat it 'cus the floer an' the table was full a buttons an' bits a card. Our Elsie stayed in to 'elp me, but I told the young uns to goo an' play in the 'orse road, 'cus they' only be in the road in 'ere and I'd gorra gerrall the buttons carded begenst Mrs Phillips came with the pram to tek 'em to the factory.

The next thing I knew, this hoity-toity missis come knocking on the doer. I doan know why 'er done that, 'cus it was open. All 'er'd gorra do was shout in. Any road, I looked up at 'er and 'er started to 'ave a goo at me about the state of the 'ouse an' about 'ow I wornt lookin' after me kids.

I looked at 'er as 'er was gooin on an' I thought, 'Who does 'er think 'er is! 'er comes traipsin' in 'ere and starts 'avin' a goo!'

I know 'er was posh, but I did lerrer 'ave it.

I sez, 'Listen missis, this 'ouse might not look much to yoh, but it's our 'ome. It's better than the work'us. An' that's wher we'd be if I dayn card buttons an' mek a mess on the floer. My old mon's dead. I've gorra babbi upstairs asleep. I've got three under six playin' out an' I've gorrour Elsie, who's seven - an' 'ers elpin' me. D'you think I wanna live like this? I int gorra choice. But I'll tell you wha', while I've got these - an' I showed 'er me 'ands - me babbies'll stay with me an' out of the work'us!.

I sez to 'er, 'This 'ouse might not 'ave a lot in

it, an' it might be a mess, but I work 'ard to keep us clean, so doan yoh think yoh can look down y' nose at me! When yoh've spent a day maidin' and washin' in the bre'us, when yoh've spent hours scrubbing the privy seat clean an' blackleaded the grate, when yoh've done that, then come an' tell me that I'm a bad mother.

'Cus I know I int!

THE LADY'S STORY

When I began to admonish the mother at her lack of care of her children, I was amazed that she answered me back. At first I was very angry. I thought to myself, 'How dare this slatternly woman talk to me like this!

But then her words began to filter through my anger. I looked around the room. It was messy, yes, but it was clean. And the woman had got a few ornaments and cheap homilies on the wall. I could see that she was working hard to be a good mother, to provide for her children, to keep her family together. It was difficult for me to accept this, but I did.

After she had her say, I apologised for my presumption. I think that shocked her more than had my harsh words earlier. We spoke and I tried to put myself in her position.

Since then I have chatted with her many times. I see now many things that I was blind to on my first visit to Floodgate Street. I see still the bad housing, the grimy atmosphere and I can smell the stink from the drains, the sewers and the factories. But I see also the hard-work, the perseverance and the endurance. I hear the laughter of the children and the rough humour of the adults, I feel the community.`

	NOT STATUTORY LISTED	YEAR	COMMENT
59 - 63 Floodgate Street	Grade A (local list)	1845 - 1850	Back to back houses

A PPENDIX

Listed buildings in Birmingham
A list of buildings with stories to tell from bygone days including historical notes for schools

NORTH AREA
(Sutton Coldfield)

ALMSHOUSES, 44 & 46 Walmley Road. Grade II
Cottages were built in 1828 financed by a local benefactress. A plaque on the cottages says 'These cottage homes were erected and endowed under a bequest from Frances Lingard, 1828'. The names 'J Riland, MA' and 'Ann Webb' can be seen on two cottages built in 1863.

ANCHORAGE ROAD Conservation Area
Several houses in the road are listed. Richard Sadler, a High Street solicitor bought 'The Anchorage' as an investment in 1870 intending the land to be developed as a housing estate. He offered the house and land surrounding it for sale as 26 building lots, with stringent conditions attached: 'No dwellinghouse shall be of less cost and value, exclusive of outbuildings, than £500'.

ASHFURLONG HALL, Tamworth Road. Grade II*
Predominantly Georgian, but traces of earlier Tudor masonry and a 'Vesey' window have been revealed within the last 20 years. In Victorian times, Thomas Colmore, magistrate and three times Warden of Sutton Coldfield, lived here and he 'exercised great influence for good in the district. He took a particular interest in the increasing problem of sewage disposal.

BAPTIST CHURCH & HALL, Victoria Road and Trinity Hill, Sutton Coldfield Conservation Area
The building was originally designed as a school in 1826 for boys and girls. The pupils' blue uniforms were provided by the Corporation. The building was designed by Mr Bateman, the Birmingham Architect. The school moved in 1981-82 to its present site in Ebrook Road.

FRONT BLOCK, BISHOP VESEY GRAMMAR SCHOOL, Lichfield Road. Grade II
Founded by Bishop Vesey in Tudor times (1528) the school moved from its original site near the Parish Church. The oldest part of the present school is Georgian, dating from when it was built in 1729: the central portion of the three-storeyed building fronts Lichfield Road.

COLLETS BROOK FARM, Tamworth Road. Grade II
The farm was originally a turnpike toll house. Is there a story behind the name 'Collet'? Is there a connection with Richard Colet who was selling land in Sutton in 1363? Is there a link with the wealthy Collett family, one of whom was Bishop Vesey's grandmother?

COUNCIL HOUSE, King Edward Square, in Sutton Coldfield Conservation Area. Built in 1863 as 'The Royal Hotel' for use by rail travellers using the newly opened line from Birmingham. Sutton Coldfield station, just below the hotel, was at that time at the end of the line, and there was a turntable to turn the engines round for their trip back to Birmingham. The building later became the Council House for Sutton Coldfield.

FORGE FARMHOUSE, Walmley Ash Lane. Grade II

FOX HILL HOUSE AND BEEHIVE KILN, Fox Hill Road. Grade II. The House (also known to local people as 'Fiddlers Hall') was built by John Valentine, brother of the composer of the folk song 'All Around My Hat'. John Valentine set up a pottery business which later failed, but the kiln still remains near the house.

THE GROVE, Grove Lane, Wishaw. Grade II* One of over fifty houses built in the 1530's by Bishop Vesey.

HIGH HEATH COTTAGE, Withy Hill Road. Grade II*
Another Bishop Vesey cottage. The cottage was then in a remote spot, possibly chosen so that the occupant could keep an eye on the unsavoury characters preying on travellers along the London Road, on the other side of the valley. It is one of the smallest cottages built by Bishop Vesey, with a single

room and a fireplace on each floor. Labourers' cottages would not normally have had the luxury of a fireplace in the attic in Tudor times.

HIGH STREET. Within Sutton Coldfield Conservation Area

HOLY TRINITY PARISH CHURCH, Coleshill Street. Grade A (local list)
Mediaeval origin; built in 1305 approximately. Norman font, originally from the church at Over Whitacre. The tower is believed to have been erected in the 15th century. In Tudor times, Bishop Vesey added two aisles and an organ. His tomb is in the church. There are several graves and memorials, including Lady Jane Pudsey (see the story about Moat House, 18th Century) and both her husbands; also Mary Ashford who was murdered in 1817 (see Appendix, Erdington, Tyburn House). Major repairs in the 18th century and alterations and extensions in the 19th century. Richly decorated ceiling by CE Bateman in 1914.

LANGLEY HALL FARM, Ox Leys Road. Grade II
The farm was once the stable block belonging to Langley Hall, dating back to around 1680. Langley Hall, in the 13th century, was the biggest moated house in Sutton. It was inherited by Edith Hore in the reign of Henry VII, and she married Rowland Pudsey. In the 17th Century (see story of Jane Pudsey and Moat House), George Pudsey built Langley Mill and created the Mill Pool in 1604, now a haven for wild life, owned by Severn Trent. The Hall was demolished in 1817, soon after it had been purchased by its owner, Sir Robert Peel. The remains of the moat may still be seen however.

The MANOR, Manor Drive. Grade II
Occupies the site of the mediaeval Manor House built by the Earls of Warwick near to the 'fair pools' (formed by Plants Brook). In Tudor times it is believed that Bishop Vesey ordered the stones from the old Manor House to be 'recycled' in order to build the bridges at Curdworth and Water Orton (see story). The bridges are still there today.

MERE GREEN CHARITY SCHOOL, Mere Green Road, Sutton Coldfield. Grade II. Once an early 19th century school, founded in 1826 for 25 boys and 25 girls, constructed by Solomon Smith, a local man. He leased two cottages to Mr and Mrs Daniel Aulton, the first Master and Mistress at the school for £10 per annum.

MINWORTH GREAVES FARM, Kingsbury Road. Grade II
At present unoccupied.

The MOAT HOUSE, 24 Lichfield Road, Sutton Coldfield, Grade II*
Built in the Queen Anne style by the stonemason and architect William Wilson for his wife, Lady Jane Pudsey, in 1679. (See story about Moat House). It has an unusual rectangular sundial on the gable end. When Jane died she was buried in the churchyard of Holy Trinity Church, but when William died, her

family did not allow him to be buried next to his wife. Her family did not, however, altogether succeed in keeping husband and wife apart after death - what William had planned makes an interesting story.

NEW HALL, Walmley Road, Walmley. Grade I
The first part of New Hall was built around 1200 and was L-shaped. The first mention of the name 'New Hall' was in 1341. For a time Bishop Vesey's brother-in-law, William Gibbons, resided there. It is reputed to be the oldest listed, inhabited moated house in England. Additions to the building were made in Tudor and Victorian times and in the latter part of the 20th century. In 1883 the owner of New Hall, Charles Chadwick, was bankrupt. The chandeliers from the Great Hall were sold to Mr Chatwin in Edgbaston. In 1885 it was known as the 'New Hall College for Boys'. Its education prepared pupils for the professional and commercial world and the healthy surroundings were exemplified by the claim that during a period of 12 months, not a single case of illness had occurred. The school closed for economic reasons in 1905. Five years later, the owner of New Hall, Walter Wilkinson, brought back the chandeliers from Edgbaston. The estate was purchased by Alfred Ernest Owen in 1923, and his son, Sir Alfred Owen, Chairman of Rubery Owen & Co Ltd, lived there with his family until his death, when the Hall was sold. It opened as a hotel in 1988. (See story). Other listed buildings at New Hall include the Chapel (Grade II); Coach House and stables (Grade II); the Gardener's Cottage (Grade II).

NEW HALL MILL, Wylde Green Road. Grade II*
The first record of the mill is in 1638 - it is still in working order. In Victorian times, the miller, Benjamin Styles, sent a loaf of bread to Queen Victoria made from the flour he had ground at the mill. His grandson, and tenant of the mill, sent a loaf to Queen Elizabeth II for her Silver Jubilee - both loaves are still in existence in the Queen's collection.

NEW SHIPTON FARM BARN, Wylde Green Road. Grade II*
Ghost Story: In 1745, an army under the Duke of Cumberland was sent in pursuit of 'Bonnie Prince Charlie'. At Tyburn, his soldiers asked a youth to give them directions, but unfortunately he could not make himself understood as he had no roof to his mouth. He was presumed to be a spy and summarily executed on the spot. His body was thrown into the Ebrook at Eachelhurst, and his head carried on a halbert to New Shipton, where it was flung in an oak tree. When the tree was felled in 1827, his skull rolled out. And so.. at the hour of dusk.. do not be surprised if you meet the headless body, drifting slowly across Wylde Green Road from the direction of New Shipton...

OLD MOOR HALL FARM, 29 Moor Hall Drive. Grade II*
This farm was the birthplace of Bishop Vesey. The substantial 14th Century stone built house has mullioned lancet windows, a circular staircase and heavy timber floor beams.

67

The OLD SMITHY, 78 Birmingham Road, Maney. Grade II

Mediaeval origin. Approximately 500 years old, the Smithy is a good example of a cruck built structure. 17th century box framing and stone work. But, was it ever a smithy? The building in the late 19th Century was owned by W Holden, whose smithy was in Jockey Road. There are foundations of a 17th Century smithy in the front garden.

PARK HOUSE, Sutton Park. Grade II

First record is c1547 when it was built and sold to John Tuttell for £40. The two ponds in the grounds of the House mark the location of a water mill which was in operation from the early 17th century. In 1668, William Addyes cut off his servant's head. In 1770 the mill was completely rebuilt when it was used as a blade mill for polishing guns during the Napoleonic Wars. In 1840 part of the mill was pulled down and the machinery sold off. The water still runs through the cellar of Park House; the two cottages next to Park House are the remains of the mill. If you look carefully in the grounds you may still see the remains of old millstones.

PEDDIMORE HALL, Peddimore Lane, Walmley Sutton Coldfield. Grade II

Mediaeval origin first recorded in 1281 this house was owned by the Arden family in 1324. It is said that William Shakespeare visited his cousins here, and that 'Henry VI and 'Love's Labours Lost' were set here. 'Our soldiers shall march through; we'll to Sutton Colfil tonight' - Falstaff, 'Henry VI Part I', Act 4, Scene 2. The present Hall was built between 1660 and 1671 and had a double moat, remains of which can still be seen. The farm's old timber framed barn dates from 1385.

PENNS HALL, Penns Lane, Sutton Coldfield (not listed)

A Joseph Penn owned a mill on the site in 1618. The first record of the Hall is in 1759 when Joseph Webster took out a lease. In the riots of 1791, the plate from the house was sunk in the lake. The house and estate have important associations with the Webster and Horsfall families, local 'ironmasters'. Joseph Webster joined forces with James Horsfall, who had exhibited high tensile piano wire at the Crystal Palace Exhibition in 1851. In 1859, the mill closed and the firm moved to its present premises in Hay Mills and produced the successful transatlantic Cable in 1866. (See story of Mary Simms, daughter of James Horsfall). A year earlier, in 1865, James Horsfall had purchased the house. Ansells brewery later bought the estate and opened the Hall as a hotel in 1950.

QUAKER COTTAGE, Wiggins Hill Road. Grade II

In 1724, the Society of Friends, better known as the Quakers, bought a plot of land and built a meeting house and an adjoining cottage. By the early 19th Century, the congregation had dwindled and the meeting house closed down. A small burial ground remains in the garden.

RAILWAY STATION, Railway Road and Station Street, Sutton Coldfield (not listed)

Sutton Coldfield's main railway station, although not listed, is in a Conservation Area. Probably one of the last remaining complete Victorian stations built in the Classic Style in the Birmingham area. The Ticket Office and Stationmaster's house were built in the early 1880's, replacing the earlier 1860 building. The doric capped chimneys have been removed from the station roof in recent years. Inside the Booking Hall, however, travellers can still look up and see an ornate modelled plaster ceiling with ivory medallions contrasting with a cobalt blue ground. In 1862 the return fare from Sutton Coldfield to Birmingham was one penny for a third class ticket. Travelling by the new steam trains cut the travelling time in half, from one hour by omnibus, to half an hour by train. The railway enabled people from smoky industrial 19th century Birmingham to visit old Sutton town and enjoy the fresh air and pleasures of Sutton Park. For many Birmingham school children, the day visit to Sutton Park became the school's annual outing.

ROYAL HOTEL, 27 High Street. Grade II

Once a Georgian town house, with a spacious garden, whose walls can still be seen. During the 1850s it was the home of William Morris Grundy, a wealthy tanner. He was a pioneer of photography and had a horse-drawn carriage which he used as a mobile dark room! At the end of the 19th century, the town house was sold and opened as the Swan Hotel. It was renamed the Royal Hotel at the turn of the century. In the late 1970's, the Berni organisation converted it to a 'Berni Royal'.

RYKNIELD STREET, Sutton Park. Ancient monument

Known as Ryknield Street or Icknield Street, this is the old Roman road which runs through Sutton Park. On its journey south it runs through Metchley (near the Queen Elizabeth Hospital), where there was a Roman Base Camp, on to Kings Norton, where it crosses the Saltway and continues on to Bourton-on-the-Water, Gloucestershire. Northwards it crosses another Roman road, Watling Street, at Wall (Letocetum) near Shenstone, Staffordshire and stretches on to south Yorkshire. There has been little archaeological research. In the Thirties a trench was dug revealing the cambered road with a surface of coarse gravel and pebbles. A number of Roman coins have been found in the area.

SHERIFOOT LANE A Roman pottery kiln was discovered in 1987 when the owners of a house in the Lane were digging a garden pond. It was the second Roman pottery kiln to be found in Birmingham. The first was at 224 Wellington Road, Handsworth. The kiln contained beer tankards, a mixing bowl studded with grit to pulverise food, other bowls and jars, and 16 boxes of broken pottery. These pieces of pottery matched those found a few miles away in Coleshill.

The STONE HOUSE, 4 Maney Hill Road. Grade II
Tudor: one of the five remaining stone houses built at Bishop Vesey's behest, it is the largest complete cottage to survive. Original oak beams, wall panelling, a spiral staircase, open fireplaces, and floorboards between main room and bedroom which could be removed to lower a coffin. Exterior built of local red sandstone with an arrow slit in the wall overlooking the main highway. Cat's paw print on original roof tile. Open one day a year to public.

THREE TUNS PUBLIC HOUSE, 19 High Street. Grade II
Has famous associations: Tudor Times: the Earl of Richmond (later Henry VII) lodged here on his way to Bosworth. Civil War: Cromwell met his officers here after the Battle of Worcester in 1651. 18th Century: Priestley sheltered here during the Birmingham Riots of 1791. The sculptor, Frederick Woodington, who worked on Nelson's Column, lived here in his early years. Fact or fiction: Do tunnels run from the cellars to the Parish Church? Is there really a ghost in the cellars?

VESEY COTTAGE, Wylde Green Road. Grade II*
15th century: one of the cottages built by Bishop Vesey in Tudor times. It was originally a ford keeper's cottage, situated where the Ebrook (Plants Brook) crosses the road. When the stream flooded, the ford keeper would be called to assist when carts and carriages were stuck in the mud. The brook is now culverted under the road.

VESEY GRANGE, Weeford Road. Grade II*
A Bishop Vesey stone house. Alterations and additions have been made, but it still retains the spiral staircase.

WARREN HOUSE FARM AND GRANARY. Grade II
Another of the remaining Vesey stone houses, built in the 16th century, still with its oak beams, thick stone walls and spiral staircase. There is a private footpath between the Farm and the old ford keeper's cottage in Wylde Green Road, which in Tudor times must have been a link between these two Vesey houses.

WARWICK HOUSE, 9 High Street, Sutton Coldfield. Grade II
Part of the High Street Conservation Area of the town. The house on the site is the later house. Walter Peyton lived in the original house, around 1618. Peyton was born in 1584 in London. He worked for the East India Company until his voyage in the 'Expedition' of 1613. His accounts of his two voyages are still in existence. It is likely that the present house was built in the early 1800s.

WATER ORTON BRIDGE, Water Orton Lane. Grade II*
Its six arches span the river Tame. It was built in approximately 1520 and paid for by Bishop Vesey. Were some of the stones from the old Sutton Coldfield Manor House used to make the bridge? (See story).

WIGGINS HILL FARM, DOVECOTE, STABLES, OLD BARN & OLD BARN COTTAGE Wiggins Hill Road. Grade II
17th century buildings with a Dutch gable on the farm.

WINCELLE, Wylde Green Road, Sutton Coldfield. Grade II
Early 15th century, black and white timber-framed house which originally stood in Wiggins Hill, Wishaw. It was moved in 1910 and 1911 to its present site.

NORTH AREA
(Perry Barr, Kingstanding, Erdington and Handsworth)

ERDINGTON ABBEY, Sutton Road, Erdington. Grade II Designed by A.E. Dempster 1880.

BROWNE'S GREEN LODGE, 126 Handsworth Wood Road. Grade II
Lodge to Browne's Green House, demolished in 1898.

ERDINGTON COTTAGE HOMES, Fentham Road, Erdington Grade II

DREWS FLOUR MILL, Grosvenor Road, Handsworth (not listed)
1886: John Drew's third flour mill (his second mill was in Drew's Lane, Washwood Heath).

ENDWOOD PUBLIC HOUSE, Hamstead Road, Handsworth. Grade II
Known as Church Hill House in 1820. Once a private residence, and home to various different owners in Victorian times, including Philip Henry Muntz.

HANDSWORTH OLD TOWN HALL, 20 Slack Lane, Handsworth. Grade II
A four bay cruck house, probably built in the 15th century. Not a town hall in the political sense - it derives its name from the 'Town End', a mediaeval district of Handsworth parish in which the hall stood. Tradition suggests Oliver Cromwell rested here. The house became a pair of tenements in the 18th century. Once the residence and office of the Overseer of the Parish, whose jobs included organising funerals and fetching a doctor for the injured. Open to the public one Saturday each month or by arrangement (021 554 1179).

HANDSWORTH HALL, Friary Road, Handsworth. Grade II
1881. Designed by Ball & Goddard, in early Tudor style for a Wesleyan Theological College. Now property of University of Aston.

HANDSWORTH NEW ROAD SCHOOL, Winson Green. Grade II. The architect was Henry Tudor Buckland, who won a competition at the start of his career with his design. He followed Martin & Chamberlain as the Education Department's architect. It closed as a school in July 1990. At present unused.

HANDSWORTH PUBLIC LIBRARY & COUNCIL HOUSE, Soho Road, Handsworth. Grade II
Late Victorian building.

HAWTHORNE HOUSE, 58 Hamstead Hall Road, Handsworth. Grade II
Georgian. Mr Bullock, Ironmaster, lived here in 1841. He had an iron foundry in West Bromwich.

The HOVEL, 192 Jerry's Lane, Erdington. Grade II
18th Century. Once an agricultural labourer's cottage, only recently 'discovered' in the grounds of a mid Victorian farm and now listed. (See story).

LAD IN THE LANE Public House, Bromford Lane, Erdington. Grade II
One of the oldest inns in the Midlands. Formerly the 'Old Green Man', the exterior has been heavily restored. One of the few buildings in Birmingham with a cruck frame. Some of the internal timbers date from 1306. The public house claims connections with the Civil War, housing both Parliamentarian and Royalist troops at different times. Local tales suggest a secret tunnel to Aston Hall.

ODEON CINEMA, Kingstanding Grade II
Designed by Harry Weedon in 1935, as the first in a chain of cinemas. Oscar Deutsch bought it and built the rest in the same style.

OSCOTT COLLEGE, Chester Road, New Oscott. Grade II*
Building began in 1835, designed by Robert Potter of Lichfield and includes work by A W N Pugin, architect of St Chad's Cathedral in Birmingham.

PYPE HAYES HOUSE, Pype Hayes Park, Erdington. Grade II
Early Stuart; Georgian porch and stables. Built by Sir Harvey Bagot in the reign of James I. Owned by James Rollaston (manufacturer of ball bearings) in 19th Century. Day Nursery during Second World War.

ROOKERY HOUSE, Rookery Park, Kingsbury Road, Birches Green, Edgbaston Grade II
Possibly built on the site of an earlier mediaeval house. The oldest part of the present house is early 18th century. In 1655 the Birch family lived there and it passed into the hands of Abraham Spooner through his marriage to Ann Birch early in the 18th century. Abraham's second wife was Anne Knight whose family were prominent ironmasters. In 1736 Anne gave birth to their son and heir, Isaac. Ten years later, Abraham Spooner and Edward Knight leased Bromford Forge and Aston Furnace from the Holtes. In 1783 Richard Spooner born at the house, later to be Birmingham's first Tory MP (1844-47), In 1816 Isaac Spooner sold the property to Brueton Gibbins, Birmingham Banker and Glass Manufacturer. The first etched plate glass doors in the country were installed at the house. Gibbins sold the house in 1848. A ballroom and a gothic style conservatory were added in the mid Victorian era. From 1905-1911, it was Erdington's Council House.

ST MARY'S CHURCH, Hamstead Road, Handsworth. Grade II*
The parish church was originally erected in the early 12th century. Parish registers date to 1558. Monuments in the churchyard to the memory of the 18th century industrialists Watt, Boulton and Murdoch. Watt has his own chapel with statue. Also in the churchyard is the grave of William Booth, executed for forgery in 1812. William's home, Booths Farm, was demolished in 1974, and the land is now part of the site of the Perry Beeches schools.

SOHO HOUSE, Soho Avenue, Handsworth. Grade II*
Mid 18th century house. The home of Matthew Boulton, innovator, manufacturer and entrepreneur of the Industrial Revolution, from 1796 until his death in 1809. Boulton introduced such new devices as heating ducts and water closets. The architect was Samuel Wyatt. Boulton's home was described as '... the resort of lords and ladies, princes and philosophers, servants and students to a far greater extent than many European courts.' A brilliant group of scientists, inventors and engineers known as the Lunar Society met here. One of them referred to the house as 'l'hotel de l'amitie sur Handsworth Heath'. It is believed to be haunted - perhaps by the ghost of Boulton's first wife, Mary who took her own life. Matthew Boulton married Mary's sister, Ann. The premises later became a Ladies' College and then a hotel. Soho House will open as a museum in 1994.

FOOTBRIDGE TO PERRY BARR LOCKS, Rowdale Road, Perry Barr. Grade II
A rural flight of locks on the Tame Valley Canal which pass under the Walsall Road. The footbridge at Rowdale Road and the Lock Keeper's Cottage at the top of the flight of locks are also listed.

TYBURN HOUSE Public House, Kingsbury Road/Chester Road, Erdington. Grade II
Present building designed by C E Bateman for the brewery, Mitchells & Butlers and built in 1930. Linked to the Mary Ashford murder case (see Holy Trinity Parish Church, Sutton Coldfield). Mary Ashford, aged 20 years, had been attending a Whit Monday Dance at Tyburn House in 1817. Her body was found the following morning in a water filled quarry pit, near the track that ran from Bell Lane (now Orphanage Road) to Penns Mill Lane (now Penns Lane). The accused, Abraham Thornton, the last person to be seen with Mary, was acquitted of her murder. Mary's brother appealed and Thornton demanded the right to 'Trial by Battel' - to fight to the death against his accuser to prove his innocence. William Ashford refused and Thornton was freed. There have, however, been reports over the years of the ghost of a young woman, walking the lanes she once knew between Erdington and Walmley.

SOUTH AREA

BELLS FARMHOUSE, 157 Bells Lane, Brandwood. Grade II*
A restored 16th century farmhouse. The site of the house was moated to the west. It is now a community centre. School visits, for history projects etc. Contact Mr J Sheard, 021-784 6408.

GREAT HALL, BIRMINGHAM UNIVERSITY, Edgbaston. Grade II*
Endowed by industrialists such as Joseph Chamberlain. One of the first duties of the University was to act as a hospital during the Great War of 1914-18.

BARBER INSTITUTE, University of Birmingham, Edgbaston Park Road. Grade II
Opened on 26 July 1939 by Queen Mary. Sir Henry Barber was a governor of Birmingham University. The Institute is now one of the finest small picture galleries in Britain.

BOTANICAL GARDENS, Westbourne Road, Edgbaston. Grade II
The land, part of the Calthorpe Estate, was obtained in 1830. The first garden was planned on the advice of John Loudon, a famous landscape designer. A magnificent elliptical conservatory was erected by Mr Jones which was considered at that time to be '... one of the finest in the kingdom.'

BOURNVILLE Village and extensions (Bournville Village: Conservation area No. 8) Includes several listed buildings, ie. Friends' Meeting House, Selly Manor, Schools)
The Bournville story really begins with Richard Tapper Cadbury, a devout Quaker who set up as a silk merchant in Bull Street in 1794. One of his ten sons, John, set up a successful beverage business in 1831 which subsequently moved to Bridge Street. John's two sons, George and Richard, saw the potential market for drinking chocolate and confectionery and in 1879 they moved the business to the countryside. They needed a site with a guaranteed supply of fresh, unpolluted water and chose an area in the fields near Bourn brook. The word 'ville' was added to 'Bourn', in deference to the quality image of French food products, and it was an apt name for the new factory with its cluster of workers' cottages built nearby. George Cadbury proceeded to buy a further 140 acres of land to build a model estate of cottages to improve the living conditions of work people from the city. The architect, William Alexander Harvey, designed almost all the houses on the estate and started building the cottages in 1895. By the end of the century the estate consisted of 330 acres with 313 cottages. In 1897, Richard Cadbury built a group of Almshouses on the southern edge of the Village. The Bournville Village Trust was set up in 1900 to preserve the estate and its 'rural aspect' - the concept of a 'Garden Village' had been born. Within a few years there were parks, places of worship, shops, an Art and Crafts Institute and schools (see story of

Bournville Junior School, 'Time Tells a Tale'). In the heart of the famous chocolate factory 'in a garden', schools and the general public can now follow the story of chocolate at 'Cadbury World' and learn about the part the Cadbury family has played in the industry. Tel 021-433 4334.

BOURNVILLE INFANTS SCHOOL, Linden Road. Grade II
BOURNVILLE JUNIOR SCHOOL, Linden Road. Grade II
built 1905 by George Cadbury (see story 'Time Tells a Tale')

EDGBASTON RESERVOIR LODGE, Reservoir Road. Grade II
Lodge to the canal feeder reservoir (also known as Rotton Park Reservoir) constructed in the 1820's to a design by the famous engineer, Thomas Telford, as part of his improvements to the Birmingham Canal. The building has architectural features similar to those used in Telford's roadside tollhouses along the main road to Holyhead (now the A5). Now used as the Ranger's Office, with possibility of school visits (021-454 1908).

GREAT STONE INN, 158 Church Road, Northfield. Grade II
Opposite St. Laurences's Church, mainly 18th century externally, but housing a late mediaeval hallhouse. Derives its name from the glacial boulder which could be found in the road outside - which has now been removed to the adjoining Pound.

The GREEN, Kings Norton. (Kings Norton Conservation Area)
Houses many of the listed buildings of great interest. The Green itself hosted the famous annual Mop Fair for centuries.

OLD GRAMMAR SCHOOL, The Green. Grade II*
Probably built as the priest's house to St. Nicolas' Church. Early 15th Century, altered. The upper storey originally upheld by pillars; the ground floor apparently underbuilt when the porch was added probably in the late 16th century.

ST. NICHOLAS' CHURCH, The Green. Grade I
Mediaeval: 12th century with monuments of the Littleton and Grevis families: There is a memorial in the graveyard to William Greves who was murdered in 1605 while collecting rents. Burial registers date back to 1546. Two Norman windows; 15th century tower and spire. The interior suffered during the time of the Reformation.

THE SARACEN'S HEAD, 81, 83 The Green. Grade II*
Mediaeval.
Its construction is half timbered, black and white, overhanging upper storey, and can be dated to around the late 15th century. Queen Henrietta Maria, wife of Charles I, stayed the night here on 10 July 1643. She was travelling south with an army of 6,000 men to support her husband during the Civil War. (See story)

HARBORNE HALL, Old Church Road, Harborne. (Harborne Old Village Conservation Area) Late 18th century. Built by Thomas Green, a nailmaker, Lord of the Manor of Harborne, for his daughter Elizabeth, wife of George Simcox on the site of an earlier house. Unfortunately she died aged 32 years in 1795 probably before the house was finished. In Victorian times, Edward Dinwoody Wilmot, wholesale jeweller, lived there for five years (1850-1855) with his large family of 10 children. His wife Sarah, died aged 40 after the birth of their tenth child, but later Edward married her sister Felicia, who died aged 31 after having three children. Edward married yet another sister, Phoebe, and in the end he had 20 children! Florence Nightingale Freeman Wilmot, one of the daughters, remained unmarried and became an artist. Edward was a friend of the preacher, George Dawson, referred to by Charles Kingsley as 'the best public speaker in England'. Edward's sister married William Roberts and they lived at the Hall until 1867. The next owner of the Hall, Charles Hart, metalworker, created the wrought iron gates for Hampton Court Palace. He commissioned John Henry Chamberlain, architect, to make alterations to the Hall. His son succeeded the family business (Messrs. Hart, Son, Peard and Co) which made the column for the 'Chamberlain clock' in Vyse Street in the Jewellery Quarter. One member of the Chamberlain family, Walter, youngest son of Joseph Chamberlain (founder of Nettlefold and Chamberlain, screw manufacturers) lived at the Hall from 1885 to 1902. He married a Canadian Society girl, Agnes Gilmour, and after a five year world tour together, they returned to live at the Hall. He commissioned the Birmingham firm of architects, Martin and Chamberlain, to make additions and alterations to the house. He was chairman of several well known companies including Guest, Keen and Nettlefold, W & T Avery Limited and Joseph Lucas Limited. He was the first chairman of Harborne Board School. His daughter, Pearl, served in the First World War as a nurse. During the war, the Hall was used as a home for Belgian refugees, and then as a military hospital, financed by the employees of W & T Avery Limited. After the war it became a boys' preparatory school, where gardening and nature study were 'much encouraged'. In 1925, the Sisters of the Retreat of the Sacred Heart bought the property. During the Second World War, nuns escaping from the German invasion of France, found refuge at the Hall. Finally, in 1988, MOSAIC, a Foundation for Education and Citizenship, rented the premises from the Sisters. The multi-faith Centre has a team of educators. The Executive Director is Dr. Mary Hall. (See story).

HAWKESLEY FARM MOATED SITE, Stokesay Grove, Longbridge. Birmingham Ancient Monument. Hawkesley Hall was bought in 1549 by the Middlemore family whose descendants lived there during the first part of the 17th century. Reputed to have been the site of a great deal of activity during the Civil War period. Only the moat now remains.

HOLY CHILD SCHOOL, Sir Harry's Road, Edgbaston. Grade II

LIFFORD HALL, Lifford Lane, Stirchley. Grade II 17th Century watermill and house enlarged and converted in the 19th century. Stone-lined water channels for the mill, recently investigated by archaeologists, were long mistaken for 'secret tunnels'. The name 'Lifford' has nothing to do with the nearby fording point of the Rea, but in fact comes from a previous owner, Viscount Lifford, who took his name from a town in Ireland. Owners: Messrs John E. Sturge Limited.

LONGBRIDGE: The Austin Village Prefabricated houses Built by Herbert Austin for his workers at Longbridge during the First World War. The wooden parts for the house came by ship from Canada and were built on site at Longbridge. The houses are still occupied over 75 years later.

METCHLEY CAMP, Vincent Drive, Edgbaston. Birmingham Ancient Monument Site of a Roman Army Base Camp, 48 AD at the city's earliest known road junction, where Ryknield Street met Roman roads from Droitwich and Penkridge. Once a 14 acre site housing about 3,000 troops in timber buildings.

MINWORTH GREAVES MANOR, Maple Road/Sycamore Road, Selly Oak. Grade II Mediaeval, 14th century cruck timber framed building, moved in 1929 from Minworth, Sutton Coldfield by George Cadbury and reconstructed on its present site, alongside Selly Manor. Open all year except December and mid June Tel: 021 472 0199.

NAILMAKERS COTTAGES, Church Hill, Northfield. Grade II (only No 6) Nailmaking has been an occupation, particularly in the Midlands, for centuries. Usually sited near rivers and canals for their ease of access for the transportation of bar iron. Many cottagers combined occupations - as did those in the cottages in Church Hill.

The ORATORY, Hagley Road, Edgbaston. Grade II Founded by a leading Victorian churchman and convert to Catholicism John Henry (later Cardinal) Newman, whose study has been preserved and may be visited by arrangement (tel 021 454 0496). The Oratory Church was built between 1907 and 1910 in Baroque style. Saintly relics include the hair shirt of Sir Thomas More and the bones of a 3rd century saint called Valentinus or St. Valentine which Newman brought back from Rome in 1847. In all, 20 memorial tablets exist in the church.

Sir Robert PEEL Statue, Pershore Road, Edgbaston. Grade II Statesman, who entered Parliament at 21 years of age. Secretary of State for Ireland, 1812 to 1818. Associated with the founding of the police force when he was Home Secretary. He was thrown from his horse in Hyde Park, London, and died from his injuries in 1850.

The POUND, 156 Church Road, Northfield. Grade II
Originally housed the stray animals of the district, for which the owners would be charged. Its unusual design makes it particularly interesting - small, brick built with grilles on the windows and door.

PRIMROSE HILL FARMHOUSE, Meadowsweet Avenue, Kings Norton. Grade II*
Late 15th century. The timber framed south and east front elevations were clad in brick in early 20th century. To the west of the farmhouse is a Grade II listed barn, probably 17th century.

The ROUNDHOUSE, 16 St James's Road, Edgbaston. Grade II

ST. BARTHOLOMEW'S CHURCH, Church Road, Edgbaston. Grade II
North aisle probably late 15th century. Registers date to 1635. The church once contained three tombs honouring the Royalist Midddlemore family, but they were destroyed by Parliamentary troops who were garrisoned at Edgbaston Hall.

ST. LAURENCE CHURCH, Church Hill, Northfield. Grade I
Dates from around 1170 and was originally thought to be dedicated to St Michael until records were found around the turn of the century at Worcester Cathedral. The church register dates to around 1560 and there is a wealth of information in the churchyard itself. (See story).

ST PETER'S CHURCH, Old Church Road, Harborne. Grade II
In existence in 1279, with parish registers dating from 1538. The artist David Cox is buried here.

ST PETER'S CE J&I SCHOOL, Old Church Road, Harborne. Grade II
Circa 1840 also former Master's House

SAREHOLE MILL, Cole Bank Road, Hall Green. Grade II
A three-storey corn mill dating from the late 18th century. The millwork dates from the late 1850's when an engine house was added. Matthew Boulton leased the property in 1762, and JRR Tolkien lived nearby from 1896 ('The Hobbit' is believed to be about this area). Restored in the 1960's. For school visits, contact the Education Officer. Tel. 021 777 6612

SELLY MANOR, Maple Road/Sycamore Road, Bournville. Grade II Mediaeval.
The family of Agnes Jouette were Lords of the tithing at Selly Manor, a sub-manor of Weoley. In 1428, complaints were made at the Manorial Court at Weoley that the Manor House of Selly was in a ruinous condition. The Lord of the Manor, Thomas Jouette, was ordered to restore it and it is thought he rebuilt the house. In Tudor Times, the house was extended. Selly Manor originally stood in Bournbook Road until it was purchased and re-erected at Bournville Green by Mr George Cadbury in 1916. Schools can visit by contacting Margaret Wellings at the site on telephone number 021 472 0199.

SELLY OAK PUMPING STATION, Bristol Road. Grade II
Rare surviving example of Victorian arrangements for Birmingham's water supply. Water was pumped by a James Watt beam engine from a borehole beneath the building, which was constructed in 1878, just after the waterworks companies were 'municipalised' - taken over by the Corporation of Birmingham. Joseph Chamberlain, who was then Mayor of Birmingham and the guiding light behind the take-over, said 'All regulated monopolies sustained by the State, in the interest of inhabitants generally, should be controlled by the representatives of the people and not left in the hands of private speculators'.

Joseph STURGE Statue, Edgbaston
Birmingham Quaker, industrialist and philanthropist, famed for his work on behalf of the slaves in the West Indies. After his death people he had helped to gain their freedom wore 'Sturge hats' as a token of gratitude.

WEOLEY CASTLE Alwold Road, Weoley Castle. Grade II & Ancient Monument (Mediaeval) In 1264 Roger de Somery was granted a licence to "fortify and crenellate" his manor house, to enclose with a stone wall and moat - it contained a gatehouse and five projecting towers. The name Weoley is old English for a wood or clearing which contains a temple. Who 'wore the patched leather shoe, rattled the mediaeval keys, or dropped the Venetian coin?' Find out by visiting the ruins and the site museum. Open March until end of October Tel: 021 427 4270. (See story by Peter Leather, "Weoley Boring?").

CENTRAL AREA

ALMHOUSES, Lenches Trust, Conybere Street, Highgate. Grade II

ARGENT CENTRE, Frederick Street, Hockley. Grade II*
The former Argent Works of 1862-63, built as a pen manufactory for QE Wiley, who installed a Turkish Bath using the excess steam from the engines in the factory. A house formerly on this site is said to be the place where the American author Washington Irving wrote his famous story 'Rip Van Winkle' in 1818.

ASTON HALL, Aston Park, Aston. Grade I
Early Jacobean. Built between 1618 and 1635 by John Thorpe for Sir Thomas Holte. King Charles I stayed here on 18 and 19 October 1642. During the Civil War, Parliamentary forces attacked in 1643 and gained entry after a three day siege, costing the lives of over seventy men. Evidence of the battle can still be seen where the main staircase was damaged by cannon fire. James Watt the Younger lived here from 1818 to 1848. In Victorian times, Selina Powell, the 'female Blondin', fell from a tightrope in Aston Park and Queen Victoria was horrified when she heard the news. The following year the Hall and Park were opened to the general public for their 'free use and enjoyment for ever'. The Hall is open all the year, and

in the winter visitors can sometimes see the rooms lit by candlelight. There is an Education Officer on site for school visits. Tel. 021 327 0062.

THOMAS ATTWOOD, Statue, Turner Street, Highgate Road, Sparkbrook. Grade II
Born in 1783, son of a steel manufacturer from Shropshire. He came to Birmingham as a member of the banking firm Spooners & Attwoods. Appointed High Bailiff of Birmingham in 1811, aged 28 years. His first home was 'The Larches', Sparkbrook, then he moved to the 'Grove', Harborne. He was a Birmingham MP for seven years, presented a Chartist petition to Parliament, supported by over a million signatures. He was a political reformer who won Birmingham its right to Parliamentary representation in 1832. There is also a new statue of Thomas Attwood, reclining on the steps in Chamberlain Square.

BARTON'S ARMS Public House, 152 High Street, Aston. Grade II*
Late Victorian: built 1900. Many Music Hall stars from the nearby Aston Hippodrome (built 1908) were allegedly regulars at the pub, including Charlie Chaplin, Laurel and Hardy, and the opera star, Caruso.

BIRMINGHAM MINT, Icknield Street, Hockley. Grade II
Founded by the Heaton family in the 1860's as the successor to Boulton's Soho Mint. Heaton coins, including some British pennies and almost the entire national bronze currency in 1876, were identified by an 'H' mintmark.

BLAKESLEY HALL, Blakesley Road, Yardley. Grade II*
A timber framed Tudor farmhouse built by Richard Smalbroke in 1590. Now a popular venue for schools studying the Tudor and Stuart periods of history (see stories in this book) it is also open to the general public.
A huge boulder, called the 'Gilbertstone' has been resited in the grounds; it was used as a boundary marker for hundreds of years... and a legend surrounds it. Tel. 021 783 2193.

BLOOMSBURY BRANCH LIBRARY, Nechells Parkway, Heartlands. Grade II
Built in 1892 as one of the city's Free Libraries. The refurbishment of the Library has just been completed. Contemporary interior designs blend in with Victorian features that have been retained, such as the old gas fittings.

BREARLEY STREET NURSERY SCHOOL, Brearley Street, Newtown (locally listed)
An unusually advanced design by William Benslyn, local government architect in the 1930's. The constraints of the small site backing on to a factory, led him to design a second floor, unusual for a nursery. This 'lifted' the building above the slum surroundings into the light and air above. (See pictures in this book by the nursery pupils).

BROADWAY SCHOOL, MASTER'S HOUSE, HALL, GATE PIERS AND RAILINGS, Whitehead Road, Aston. Grade II
Very richly modelled design for a Victorian Board School. Principally buff terracotta and red brick, combining English Baroque with Art Nouveau. Now a secondary school.

CANNON HILL HOUSE, Cannon Hill Park, Pershore Road, Grade II
The bridge over the lake and the bandstand in the park are also listed. The park was given to the City in 1878 by Louisa Anne Ryland.

CONVENT OF OUR LADY OF MERCY, 98 Hunter's Road, Lozells. Grade II*
Several houses (between Nos. 100 and 140) in Hunter's Road are also listed, Grade II.

GOLDEN LION INN, Cannon Hill Park, Edgbaston. Grade II
Removed from Deritend to Cannon Hill Park in 1911. Probably early 16th Century with 18th Century alterations. 18th Century painted inn sign.

GUILD HOUSE, DERITEND (Old Crown Inn), High Street, Deritend. Grade II*. Mediaeval origin: first phase of the building dates between 1450 and 1500. It was used as a school in the 16th century with a house for the Master and the Usher. In a deed of 1589 the building was referred to as the 'Crown Inn' and was sold by Richard Smalbroke of Yardley to John and Ann Dixon of Birmingham. In April 1643 Prince Rupert's Cavaliers fought outside. The Inn was known as 'The Sign of the Crown' in 1666. It was altered and extended in 1862. In 1925 it was sold to the Holt Brewery, and subsequently to Ansells, who have recently sold the premises to a private owner.

HIGHBURY HALL, Yew Tree Road, Moseley. Grade II*
Late Victorian: designed by John Henry Chamberlain for the Rt Hon Joseph Chamberlain (no relation) who was an MP from 1880 to 1914. Famous visitors to Highbury included Beatrix Potter and the young Winston Churchill when he was a war correspondent covering events in South Africa. It became a hospital in 1915 during the First World War, and later an old people's home. There is a ghost story associated with the building. Occasional open days to the public; Victorian gardens open all the year round. Tel 021 449 6549.

LADYPOOL JUNIOR AND INFANT SCHOOL, Stratford Road, Highgate. Grade II*
Victorian red brick with terracotta dressings and timber framing with gables: designed in 1885 by Martin and Chamberlain in their imaginative polychrome Gothic style. Tiled roof surmounted by an ingeniously louvred and spired ventilation-cum-bell tower. Original Master's house with half timber details to gables. Still in use as a school.

LLOYD'S BANK AND CHAMBERS, 61-65 Villa Road, Lozells. Grade II

LLOYD'S FARMHOUSE, Farm Park, Sampson Road, Sparkbrook. Grade II*
A fine mid-18th century house, built by Sampson Lloyd II, as the main residence of the Birmingham branch of the Lloyd family from 1742 to 1912. Lloyd's Farm is one of the rare surviving Georgian buildings in the City. It still retains its grounds with a formal avenue of elms leading up to the original entrance. (See story)

MALTHOUSE FARM, 457 Alcester Road South, Kings Heath. Grade II

MOSELEY HALL HOSPITAL, Alcester Road. Grade II
(Moseley Conservation Area)
Moseley Park and Pool, landscaped by Humphrey Repton.

MOSELEY HALL, COWHOUSE. Grade II

MOSELEY HALL DOVECOTE, 181 Alcester Road, Moseley. Grade II. Early 18th Century. An octagonal red brick building standing at the entrance to Moseley Hall Hospital. The pigeons and doves were originally a source of fresh meat in winter before the invention of refrigerators. Open Easter until the end of September. Tel 021 449 2133.

MOSELEY SCHOOL (West Wing), Wake Green Road. Grade II

NECHELLS PUBLIC SWIMMING BATHS, Nechells Park Road. Grade II
Opened in 1910 by Arthur Harrison, customers were given thirty minutes each to have a bath. Fourteen of the original washing baths are still in use.

PERROTT'S FOLLY ('The Monument'), Waterworks Road, Edgbaston. Grade II*
Named after John Perrott who had the folly built in 1758 in the middle of the mediaeval Rotton Park Estate. The tall tower is 29m high and has 139 steps to climb up to the top. No one really knows why he built it: was it to look down on his wife's grave in St Philip's Churchyard? (no longer possible as tower blocks ring the city centre); or watch over his sweetheart's house at Five Ways? Or gaze in the direction of his ancestral home in Belbroughton, beyond the Clent Hills? Or was it for his daughter Catherine, so she could watch him hunting in the fields of Ladywood below? John Perrott died there in April 1776 and the estate passed to Catherine's husband. In 1851 Joseph Gillott, the wealthy penmaker, bought the estate. In 1884 it was one of the world's first weather stations: Abraham Follet Osler, inventor of the self regulating wind gauge decided it would be the ideal place to do accurate meteorological observations. Open Easter until the end of September on Sundays and Bank Holiday Mondays. Admission £1.

PLOUGH AND HARROW HOTEL, Hagley Road, Edgbaston. Grade II

PUMPHOUSE, Waterworks Road, Edgbaston. Grade II
Victorian pumphouse, designed by JH Chamberlain and W Martin in 1870, for the Birmingham Waterworks Company, which was taken over by the Corporation in 1876.

RECTORY FARM, Ragley Drive, Sheldon. Grade II
17th Century. From 1690-1729 home of Dr Thomas Bray, Rector of St Giles' Church and founder of the SPCK (Society for the Promotion of Christian Knowledge) in 1698 and the Society for the Propagation of the Gospel in Foreign Parts in 1701. Bray went to Maryland, America, where he set up 16 libraries. He was also a teacher and he helped to form church schools for the children of the poor. He also looked into prison reform. He died in 1730 and in his will left a library of books for the use of the Rector of Sheldon for ever - they are in the Central Library, Birmingham, for safekeeping. (See story by Brays School).

ST AGATHA'S CHURCH, Stratford Road, Sparkbrook. Grade I

ST CYPRIAN & ST CHAD, The Fordrough, Hay Mills. Grade II
Designed by Martin and Chamberlain in 1873-4, and built by James Horsfall, mill owner, at the entrance to his factory (now Webster and Horsfall Limited). There is a monument to James Horsfall's daughter Mary, young wife of the vicar of St. Cyprian's, the Rev G H Simms who died in 1877. (See story of Mary Simms in this book). Church damaged during the war in 1940, but since has been restored. It is built over a millrace from the river Cole. The church is open for visitors every Saturday, between 11am and 2pm.

ST EDBURGHA'S CHURCH, Church Road, Yardley. Grade I
The parish church of Yardley - said to have been founded by St Edburgha, a Saxon princess, grand daughter of Alfred the Great. It includes work from the 13th, 14th and 15th centuries. Katherine of Aragon once held the Manor of Yardley, and in the church there is a carved Tudor rose, the emblem of Henry VIII, and a pomegranate, emblem of Granada in Spain, Katherine's place of origin.

ST JOSEPH'S CHURCH, Thimblemill Lane, Nechells. Grade II
The original chapel on the hill was designed by A W Pugin in 1850 (who worked on the Houses of Parliament). The building was too small to accommodate the growing parish, and in 1870 a six day bazaar was held in Birmingham Town Hall to raise money for a larger church. The Pope sent a cameo brooch and a silver medal to help the appeal. Pugin's son, Edward, designed the extensions and the new church of St. Joseph's was officially opened on the feast day of St. Joseph, 21 April 1872. (See story).

ST PAUL'S CHURCH, St Paul's Square, Hockley. Grade I. Georgian, built in the 1770's on land given by the Colmore family. After the death of his first wife, Matthew Boulton married her sister, Ann, at this church. James Watt worshipped there. (See story)

ST. PETER'S COLLEGE, College Road, Saltley. Grade II

SCHOOL OF JEWELLERY AND SILVERSMITHING, 82-86 Vittoria Street, Hockley. Grade II
Victorian 'Gothic Style" building circa 1865 designed by JG Bland and built as a jeweller's workshop and offices. The school, founded in 1890, took over the building in 1891.

SHELDON HALL FARM BARN, Cooks Lane, Tile Cross. Grade II. 18th century.

STRATFORD HOUSE, Stratford Place, Highgate. Grade II* and scheduled ancient monument. Remarkable survival of a late Tudor manor house, built in 1601 for Ambrose Rotton and his wife Bridget.

SUMMERFIELD COMMUNITY CENTRE, Winson Green Road, Winson Green. Grade II
Opened as Dudley Road Board School in 1878. The school, now known as Summerfield JI School, has moved into a new building nearby in Cuthbert Road and the old school building is a community centre.

TRUST SCHOOL (formerly the Old Grammar School), 422, 424 Church Road, Yardley. Grade II* Early Tudor building: closed as a school in 1908. 19th century additions.

CITY CENTRE AREA

ACCIDENT HOSPITAL, Bath Row. Grade II
The oldest part of the complex is also Birmingham's oldest surviving hospital building, the Queen's hospital of 1840. Much of the money for it was donated by a Rev Dr Warneford, whose coat-of-arms appears over the entrance. The motto reads 'Cruce quam muro tutior' meaning "I am protected by the Cross as by a wall".

12 AMPTON ROAD AND STABLES, Edgbaston. Grade II*
Dated 1855, mid Victorian town house, designed and built by John Henry Chamberlain, architect, for himself. The gothic detail of the stables matches the house, and the monogram JMC can be seen on the building.

BENNETT'S HILL (Colmore Row & Environs Conservation Area)
One of Birmingham's few remaining Georgian streets, laid out in the 1820s, with a number of original buildings at the Colmore Row end.
● Number 10 The Sun Insurance Company was founded here in 1710
● Numbers 11-12 Birthplace of Sir Edward Burne-Jones, artist
● Numbers 26-33 Midland Bank building Grade II. Built in 1830 as the HQ of the Birmingham Banking Company.

BERROW COURT HOTEL, Berrow Drive, Edgbaston. Grade II*
Architect JH Chamberlain. Built circa 1870 as a substantial private Victorian family house.

BRASSHOUSE, 44 Broad Street. Grade II
Built in 1781 as the Birmingham Brasshouse.

BREWMASTERS'S HOUSE, Broad Street (Within the International Convention Centre). Grade II Circa 1800 house.

CANAL AQUEDUCT, Holliday Street. Grade II
Dated 1870. Cast iron framed aqueduct taking canal from Gas Street Basin over the road.

CANAL SIDE WAREHOUSE, Fazeley Street. Grade II
Red brick canalside warehouse built around 1840.

CHAMBERLAIN SQUARE
i) Joseph Chamberlain Memorial. Grade II Gabled tower and spire in 13th century French Gothic style. Portland stone. Wall tracery by Pre-Raphaelite sculptor Thomas Woolner. Erected in 1880 to commemorate Joseph Chamberlain's services to the Town Council between 1869 and 1876.
ii) George Dawson statue and surrounding railings. Grade II George Dawson was a local preacher who helped to found the Public Library.

COLLEGE OF ARTS AND CRAFTS, Margaret Street. Grade I
Designed by Martin and Chamberlain, 1881-5, Gothic style. Now used by the University of Central England as their Fine Art Annexe.

CORPORATION STREET (No. 153 Murdoch Chambers and Nos. 155-161 Pitman Chambers). Grade II*
Designed 1896-7 by J Crouch and E Butler partly for A R Dean, manufacturer of much of the furniture for Crouch and Butler's houses and partly for a vegetarian restaurant. Arts and Crafts style.

COUNCIL HOUSE, BIRMINGHAM. Grade II*
Designed in an open competition. Winning architect was H R Yeoville Thomason. Design is that of a Venetian Palace in Classical Renaissance style. Foundation stone laid by Lord Mayor, Joseph Chamberlain in 1874.
When King Edward VII and Queen Alexandra visited the City to open Birmingham University, an ornate ceremonial lift was installed in 1909 in the Entrance Hall of the Council House to accommodate the infirm King. The story goes that the King refused to use the lift and it remains virtually unused today.

COUNCIL HOUSE CLOCK (BIG BRUM) Grade II*
Made and erected in 1885. The clock movement is contained in a cast iron frame about 8' long and 3' wide. It used to chime regularly but patients at a nearby private hospital in Newhall Street complained bitterly to the Lord Mayor of Birmingham and the Editor of the Daily Post about the chimes keeping them awake. W Pugin Thornton, in hospital following an abdominal operation writes, "In the City the wretched stumbling block to getting rapidly well is the repeated quarter-hour horror of the slowly passing night". It was decided to cut off the chiming mechanism between 7.30pm and 5.00am. This also pleased music lovers whose enjoyment of a concert at the Town Hall had been seriously marred by Big Brum's chimes, particularly during a quiet passage.

COUNTY COURT, Corporation Street. Grade II
Designed in 1882 by James Williamson Stone in Italianate Palazzo style.

CURZON STREET RAILWAY STATION,
1 Curzon Street/New Canal Street. Grade I
The entrance building to Birmingham's first main railway station, opened in 1838 and designed by Sir Phillip Hardwick as a counterpart to his now notorious Euston Arch at Euston Station in London. The demolition of the Arch in the 1960's is supposed to have sparked off the current Conservation Movement.

DEVONSHIRE HOUSE, Digbeth. Grade II
In 1837, Alfred Bird, a chemist, devised a way of producing custard without using eggs as his wife was allergic to them. This took place in a small shop near the Bull Ring. He later became Sir Alfred Bird, and he established his custard factory at Devonshire Works in 1902.

EDEN PLACE, Four Telephone Kiosks. Grade II

GAS RETORT HOUSE, 39 Gas Street. Grade II*
An early gas manufacturing plant, dating from 1822, which may well be the oldest in existence. Designed by Samuel Clegg, a former apprentice of gas experimenter William Murdoch.

GENERAL POST OFFICE BUILDING, Victoria Square. Grade II
Design by Sir Henry Tanner based on a French chateau and built of Coxbench Stone. Opened in 1890. It weathered to a drab black after years in the polluted industrial atmosphere of the city, prior to the Clean Air Acts of 1955-56. Refurbished by the Trustee Savings Bank in 1990. It is now their head office.

GRAND HOTEL, Colmore Row (not statutorily listed)
Erected shortly before 1878 from the plans of Thomas Plevins, a Birmingham architect. The hotel was officially opened in 1879. From 1889 to 1890 the building was reconstructed by Messrs Martin & Chamberlain, architects. The columns at the entrance are of Shap Granite from the Lake District.

GREAT WESTERN ARCADE, Colmore Row. Grade II
Built over a railway tunnel in 1876 and designed by Mr WH Ward. It was first illuminated on 19 September 1876 in the presence of the Lord Mayor. The original glass roof was destroyed in the Second World War.

GUILD HOUSE, 43-45 Great Charles Street, Queensway/New Market Street. Grade II*

GUN BARREL PROOF HOUSE, Banbury Street. Grade II
Built in 1813 by John Horton. Birmingham supplied two-thirds of the British firearms during the Napoleonic Wars. In 1888 a nasty accident was reported when a George Thornhill had his head blown off.

MIDLAND BANK BUILDING (now Dillons Bookstore), 128 New Street. Grade II
The Midland Bank was founded by Charles Geach in 1836. Geach had originally been employed by the Bank of England. By the age of 28 he realised his prospects of promotion were limited and he decided that the only way to improve his position was by starting his own bank.
Geach rented a site at 30 Union Street and the Birmingham and Midland Bank opened its doors to the public on August 15. Eighteen months later the Bank moved to new larger premises higher up Union Street costing £6,300.
32 years later, with business prospering and the staff numbers increasing from three to fourteen, Midland Bank's premises in Union Street became overcrowded. In 1865 local architect Edward Holmes drew the Midland Bank's board's attention to an available site in New Street. Midland's directors quickly acquired the leasehold from the governors of King Edward's School and in the following December they commissioned Holmes to design a head office for the site. Three and a half years later the building was completed and opened for business on July 20 1869. The total final cost of £25,745 was more than twice the figure the directors had originally envisaged. Within only five years of the move to the New Street building, the continuing growth of the business made it necessary to extend the building.
The magnificent Midland Bank was sold and developed for Dillons The Bookstore at a cost of some £4.5m in 1993. (See story).

NEEDLESS ALLEY (Nos. 9-15). Grade II 'May owe its curious shape to the fact that it was once a fordrough between open field strips' (Victor Skipp in his History of Greater Birmingham)

NELSON'S MONUMENT, St Martin's Circus, Bull Ring. Grade II*
Designed by Richard Westmacott and unveiled on 24 October 1809. Nelson had previously visited Birmingham in August 1802 and was enthusiastically received wherever he went.

NEW HALL WORKS, George Street. Grade II
Large Victorian red brick factory, built c.1860-70. Building surmounted by Royal Arms.

OLD REPERTORY THEATRE, Station Street/ Hinckley Street. Grade II
Built at the expense of Sir Barry Jackson, it opened on 15 February 1913 with 'Twelfth Night'. It has close links with George Bernard Shaw in the 1920's and 1930s, and with a leading dramatist, John Drinkwater. Laurence Olivier arrived at the 'Rep' in December 1926 and spent two and a half years of his early career there.

OOZELLS ST SCHOOL, Brindley Place. Grade II
A former board school, designed by Martin and Chamberlain, in 1877 in the Ruskinian Gothic style.

POLICE CELLS, Coleridge Passage, Steelhouse Lane. Grade II
Late 19th century. Rumour has it that 100 cells lie beneath the courts and Steelhouse Lane. Would anyone like to count them?.

QUEENS COLLEGE CHAMBERS, Paradise Street. Grade II
Gothic style architecture, refaced in 1904 in ornate brick and terracotta with gables and oriels. Founded as a small medical school to train local people at moderate costs, by a surgeon, W Sands Cox. He moved to this building in 1834 which was financed by a wealthy clergyman, Dr S W Warneford and both medical and theological training was provided. Mason College (now University of Birmingham) removed the science and medical training in 1892, leaving it as an Anglican training college.

ROYAL DEAF SCHOOL, 34 Calthorpe Road, Edgbaston. Grade II
Classical early Calthorpe Estate villa of around 1815.

ST CHAD'S CATHEDRAL, Queensway
In 1838, Bishop Walsh appointed AW Pugin to design the first Roman Catholic cathedral to be built in Britain since the Reformation. Many of the cathedral's contents are older than the building: the 15th century Flemish pulpit, for example.

ST MARTIN'S IN THE BULL RING. Grade II*
The Bull Ring was originally Birmingham's village green and focal point of the markets area since the 12th century. The church's origins are early mediaeval, 13th century, and it is the Mother Church of Birmingham. Inside is the oldest monument in the city, an effigy of Lord of the Manor, Sir William de Bermingham, dated 1325. The Church was rebuilt in 1873, designed by J A Chatwin (who also worked on the Houses of Parliament). In April 1941 St Martin's suffered bomb damage but the Burne-Jones stained glass window was saved.

ST PHILIP'S CATHEDRAL. Grade I
Built in English Baroque style, designed by Thomas Archer. The tower and dome were consecrated in 1715 and completed by means of a contribution from George I. Sir Richard Gough had the idea for this donation, so part of his crest, a boar's head, was added to the weather vane. In 1884 Archer's shallow apse was replaced by a chancel designed by Chatwin. Elevated to cathedral status in 1905. Restored after war damage. Windows designed by Burne-Jones and made by William Morris. The whole building was refaced in 1957 because of the poor condition of the original Warwickshire stone. In 1976 a paved area was set outside, given to the citizens of Birmingham after the public house bombings in 1974.

ST PHILIPS' MONUMENTS. Grade II
There is a memorial pillar to John Heap and William Badger who were killed in 1833 while working on the Town Hall (see Town Hall). The smallest stone in the churchyard is that of Nanetta Stocker, who was only 33 inches tall at her death in 1819. The Burnaby Obelisk is named after Frederick Burnaby, a Victorian military man. There is also the statue of Charles Gore, the first Bishop of Birmimgham.

ST THOMAS' CHURCH (remains), Bath Row. Grade II
Completed in 1829. At this time, Holloway Head was almost entirely rural, described as a breezy upland on which could be seen the once famous windmill. In July 1838, Chartist Rioters tore down railings of the church to use as weapons. Afterwards, as a security measure an 'eighteen pounder' piece of artillery was placed nearby. The church was severely damaged in the Second World War. Local school children helped to design a Peace Garden in the ruins as a memorial.

TOWN HALL, Victoria Square. Grade I
Designed by Joseph A Hansom (of Hansom Cab fame) and E Welch who won a competition for their design in 1830. The design is a copy of the Temple of Castor and Pollux in the Roman Forum. Built of brick, faced with Anglesey Marble, a grey limestone from Beaumaris. Coral fossils may be found upon closer examination! Building started in 1832: during construction work a pedestal fell on two workmen and killed them. They are buried in St Philip's churchyard under the stone which crushed them, which was used as a memorial stone (see St Philip's Cathedral). The building opened in 1834.

VICTORIA LAW COURTS, Corporation Street. Grade I
Designed by Aston Webb and Ingress Bell. The Courts were built by a Birmingham firm, John Bowen and Sons. The red terracotta on the outside of the building was moulded and supplied by a firm at Ruabon, North Wales. On 23 March 1887 Queen Victoria came to Birmingham to lay the foundation stone. The visit was a great occasion with a procession, fanfares and presentations. Queen's Corner commemorates this visit. The courts were opened by the Prince and Princess of Wales on 21 July 1891. (See story).

USEFUL RESOURCES

Avoncroft Museum of Buildings
Stoke Heath
Bromsgrove
Worcestershire
Tel: Bromsgrove 31363

Architects - Royal Institute of British
66 Portland Place
London W1N 4AD
Tel: 071 580 5533

Bells Farm Community Association
c/o Mr J Sheard
43 Croft Road
Yardley
Birmingham B26 1SQ
Tel: 021 784 6408

Conservation Group
Department of Planning and Architecture
Baskerville House
Broad Street
Birmingham B1 2NA
Tel: 021 235 4506

Civic Trust
17 Carlton House Terrace
London SW1Y 5AW
Tel: 071 930 0914

Geoff Wright
Head of City Centre Planning
Department of Planning and Architecture
Baskerville House
Broad Street
Birmingham B1 2NA
Tel: 021 235 3075

The National Trust Birmingham Association
Hon Secretary: Rex Knight   Severn Regional Office
26 Swarthmore Road   Mythe End House
Selly Oak   Tewkesbury
Birmingham B29 4JS   Glos GL20 6EB
Tel: 021 476 6733

The Bournville Village Trust Group
Oak Tree Lane
Bournville
Birmingham B15 6BU
Tel: 021 472 3831

Victorian Society
Chairman: Dr D Low
1 Melville Road
Edgbaston
Birmingham B16 9LN
Tel 021 455 0443

Enterprise Club (Industrial Archaeology Group)
Hon Secretary: G L A Price
99 Salisbury Road
Smethwick
Warley
West Midlands B66 3RX
Tel: 021 235 3153 (Business)

The Georgian Group
37 Spital Square
London
E1 6DY

Historical Association (Birmingham Branch)
Hon Secretary: Mrs S E Armstrong
34 Cedarwood Road
Dudley
West Midlands DY3 2JD
Tel: 0902 885625

Railway and Canal History Society W M Group
Hon Secretary: Ms Meriel Cooling
9 Berberry Close
Bournville
Birmingham B30 1TB
Tel: 021 459 9643

Urban Studies Committee Birmingham
c/o Dr C Upton
Local Studies Department
Central Library
Birmingham B3 3HQ
Tel: 021 235 4220

Dr C Chinn
School of History
University of Birmingham
Edgbaston
Birmingham B15 2CT

Department of the Environment
Five Ways Tower
Frederick Road
Edgbaston
Birmingham B15 1YT
Tel: 021 626 2000

Midland History Resource Collection
Main Library
Newman College
Bartley Green
Birmingham B32 3NT
Tel: 021 476 1181 ext 208

Ken Glen, Education Officer
English Heritage
Keysign House
429 Oxford Street
London W1R 2HD
Tel: 071 973 3442/3

The Schools Library Service
Ellen Street
Hockley
Birmingham
Tel: 021 515 3939/1900

Royal Town Planning Institute
26 Portland Place
London
W1N 4BE
Tel: 021 071 636 9107

Selly Manor Museum
corner of Maple Road and Sycamore Road
Bournville
Birmingham
Tel: 021 472 0199

Thirties Society
58 Crescent Lane
London
SW4 9PU
Tel: 021 071 738 8380

Junior Education Magazine
Scholastic Publications Ltd
Villiers House
Clarendon Avenue
Leamington Spa
Warwickshire CV32 5PR

Birmingham Curriculum Support Service
Martineau Education Centre
Balden Road
Harborne
Birmingham B32 2EH
Tel: 021 428 1167

Schools Liaison
Birmingham Museum and Art Gallery
Chamberlain Square
Birmingham B3 3DH

Tel: 021 235 4618
Jewellery Quarter Discovery Centre
77-79 Vyse Street
Hockley
Birmingham
Tel: 021 554 3598

BRANCH LIBRARIES IN BIRMINGHAM WITH A USEFUL LOCAL HISTORY COLLECTION

Acocks Green
Shirley Road
Birmingham B27 7XH
Tel: 021 706 1738

Balsall Heath
Moseley Road
Birmingham B12 9BX
Tel: 021 440 1962

Castle Vale
Turnhouse Road
Birmingham B35 6PR
Tel: 021 747 7335

Erdington
Orphanage Road
Birmingham B24 9HP
Tel: 021 373 0798

Hall Green
1221 Stratford Road
Birmingham B28 9AD
Tel: 021 777 6633

Handsworth
Soho Road
Birmingham B21 9DP
Tel: 021 554 1185

Harborne
High Street
Birmingham B17 9QG
Tel: 021 427 1596

Kings Heath
High Street
Birmingham B14 7SW
Tel: 021 444 1515

Kings Norton
Pershore Road South
Birmingham B30 3EU
Tel: 021 458 1532

Kingstanding
Kingstanding Road
Birmingham B44 9ST
Tel: 021 354 5193

Nechells Green
Nechells Parkway
Birmingham B7 4PT
Tel: 021 359 3466

Northfield
Church Road
Birmingham B31 2LB
Tel: 021 475 1007

Perry Common
College Road
Birmingham B44 0HH
Tel: 021 373 0481

Quinton
Community Centre
Ridgacre Road
Birmingham B32 2TW
Tel: 021 427 7400

Selly Oak
669 Bristol Road
Birmingham B29 6AE
Tel: 021 472 0403

Shard End
Shustoke Road
Birmingham B34 7BA
Tel: 021 747 6779

Sheldon
Brays Road
Birmingham B26 2RJ
Tel: 021 743 3512

Small Heath
School and Community Centre
Muntz Street
Birmingham B10 9RX
Tel: 021 773 6131 ext 127

South Yardley
Yardley Road
Birmingham B25 8LT
Tel: 021 706 1944

Sparkhill
Stratford Road
Birmingham B11 4EA
Tel: 021 772 1134

Stirchley
Bournville Lane
Birmingham B30 2JT
Tel: 021 458 1534

Tower Hill
Tower Hill
Birmingham B42 1LG
Tel: 021 357 1948

Ward End
Washwood Heath Road
Birmingham B8 2HF
Tel: 021 327 0366

BIRMINGHAM MUSEUMS SERVICE SITES AND OTHER LOCAL MUSEUMS

Aston Hall
Aston Park
Birmingham B6 6JD
Tel: 021 327 0062

Blakesley Hall
Blakesley Road
Yardley
Birmingham B25 8RN
Tel: 021 783 2193

Sarehole Mill
Colebank Road
Moseley
Birmingham B13 0BD
Tel: 021 777 6612

Weoley Castle
Alwold Road
Weoley Castle
Birmingham B29 5RX
Tel: 021 427 4270

Highbury
Yew Tree Lane
Moseley
Birmingham B13 8QG
Tel: 021 449 6549

Minworth Greaves and Selly Manor
Bournville
Birmingham B30
Tel: 021 472 3831

LOCAL HISTORY SOCIETIES

Acocks Green Local History Society
Miss L O'Dell
1 Meadow Grove
Olton
Solihull
West Midlands B92 7JD

Balsall Heath Local History Society
Mrs V Bramwell
10 Ivy Avenue
(off Runcorn Road)
Balsall Heath
Birmingham B12 8RL

Barr and Aston Local History Society
Mrs J M Carr
c/o Tower Hill Library
Tower Hill

Birmingham B42 1LG
Birmingham and Warwickshire Archaeological Society
Mr A Wilson
41 Holifast Road
Wylde Green
Sutton Coldfield
West Midlands B72 1AP

Birmingham Civic Society
Mr D Lakin
c/o The Birmingham Post and Mail
Colmore Circus Queensway
Birmingham B4

Birmingham Urban Studies Committee
Mr A Blizzard
c/o Local Studies Department
Central Library
Birmingham B3 3HQ

The Bournville Society
Mrs J M Wood
178 Sellywood Road
Bournville
Birmingham B30 1TJ

Duddeston and Nechells Local History Group
c/o Church of God of Prophecy
Long Acre
Nechells
Birmingham

Erdington Historical Society
Miss M Baxter
c/o Sutton Coldfield Library
Lower Parade
Sutton Coldfield
West Midlands B72 1XX

Hall Green Local History Society
Mr E Gilmore
103 Southam Road
Hall Green
Birmingham B28 0AB

Handsworth Historical Society
Mrs P J Burkill
45 Stockwell Road
Handsworth
Birmingham B21 9RL

Harborne Society
Mrs J Buchan
50 Margaret Grove
Harborne
Birmingham B17 9JL

Kings Heath Local History Society
Mrs J Rhodes
c/o Kings Heath Library
High Street
Kings Heath

Birmingham B14 7SW
Kings Norton Local History Society
Miss M Murray
196 Northfield Road
Birmingham B30 1FA

Moor Street Station Historical Society
c/o Birmingham Railway Museum
670 Warwick Road
Tyseley
Birmingham B11 2HL

Moseley Society
Mrs F Adams
36 Grove Avenue
Moseley
Birmingham B13 9RY

The Northfield Society
Mrs B Prettyman
89 Steel Road
Birmingham B31 2RQ

Selly Oak Local Studies Group
c/o Selly Oak Library
669 Bristol Road
Selly Oak
Birmingham B29 6AE

Small Heath Local History Society
Mrs M Reeves
c/o Small Heath Library
Muntz Street
Birmingham B10 9XR

Sutton Coldfield Civic Society
Mr M D Sumper
192 Dower Road
Sutton Coldfield
West Midlands B75 6TB

Sutton Coldfield Local History Research Group
Miss M Baxter
Sutton Library
Lower Parade
Sutton Coldfield
West Midlands B72 1XX

Yardley Conservation Society
Mr K Lawley
381 Church Road
Yardley
Birmingham B33 8PA

BIBLIOGRAPHY

Ainsworth B	Aston Cross and its Clocks.Birmingham Historian No 8 ISBN 00953 70909
Arkinstall,M J	The Dictionary of a Great City
Bird, V	Portrait of Birmingham ISBN 07091 45820 Hale,3rd edition1979 Streetwise: Street names in and around Birmingham ISBN 1-869922-11-5
Birmingham City Council	Heritage Education Pack - useful information for teachers using local resources for teaching National Curriculum history compiled by the Planning and Architecture and Education Departments. Published 1993. Price £5. Available from Public Liaison, Planning and Architecture, Tel 021 235 3332.
Dent, R K	Old and New Birmingham (3 volumes) Republished 1972
Douglas Alton	Birmingham At War - Volume I and Volume II Published by Brewin Books.
Everitt, A E (1986)	Town & Country in the Victorian West Midlands: Watercolours and Drawings of A E Everitt of Birmingham 1824-1882 Birmingham Museum and Art Gallery ISBN 0709301 413
Fairclough, O	The Grand Old Mansion: The Holtes and Their Successors at Aston Hall 1618-1864 ISBN 07093 01227
Fairn, A	A History of Moseley, St Mary's Church Council, 1973
Groves, P	Exploring Birmingham. A Guided tour. ISBN 1-869922-00-X
Heard, I	Developing Birmingham 1889-1989: 100 Years of City Planning. Published by Brewin Books
Henslowe, Philip	Ninety Years On: An account of the Bournville Village Trust (Revised 1991) published Bournville Village Trust ISBN 0 905458-11-7
Heritage Newspapers Ltd	Bi-monthly newspaper called Bygone Birmingham. Available from Terry Wardle, Editor, Heritage Newspapers Ltd, China Court Business Centre, Ladywell Walk, Birmingham, B5 4RX. Tel 0905 358718 for past issues.
Horsfall, John	'The Iron Masters of Penns',published Kineton: The Roundwood Press 1971 ISBN 9000093-29-3
Hutton, W	An History of Birmingham, EP Publishing, 1976
Jones, Douglas V	The Royal Town of Sutton Coldfield: A Commemorative History (published 1973) Westwood Press
	Walmley & Its Surroundings, published Westwood Press ISBN 0-9948025-11-5
	The Story of Erdington, Westwood Press, 1985
	Edgbaston As It Was, Westwood Press, 1986 Sidelights on a City, Brewin Books 1989
Lea, Roger	Scenes from Sutton's Past, published Westwood Press ISBN 0 948025 10 7
Little, B	Birmingham Buildings. The Architectural Story of a Midland City ISBN 07153 52954

Maddern, E	A Teacher's Guide to Storytelling at Historic Sites. English Heritage ISBN 1850 743789
Mahar, A	Memories of Balsall Heath, Highgate and Sparkbrook, TASC 1983
Meachem, R C	Victorian Hamstead, Brewin Books 1988
Prevsner and Wedgewood, A	The Buildings of England: Warwickshire, Penguin 1966
Price, V J	The Bull Ring Remembered, Brewin Books Old Ladywood Remembered, Brewin Books Handsworth Remembered, Brewin Books Aston Remembered, Brewin Books
Simpson, Rev	Parish Church of St Cyprian, Hay Mills (Booklet, proceeds to church)
Skipp, Victor	Medieval Yardley, 1970 The Making of Victorian Birmingham, 1983 A History of Greater Birmingham down to 1830 ISBN 0-9506998-0-2, 1980
Whybrow, J	How does your Birmingham grow? ISBN 095024 5909
Wilkins, R	Turrets, Towels & Taps. Birmingham Museum and Art Gallery ISBN 07093 01219
Wilmot, Frances	The History of Harborne Hall. Meridian Books ISBN 1 869922 17 4
Wright, D	An account of Harborne to 1891, BPL 1987
Zuckerman, J & Eley, G	Birmingham Heritage ISBN 085664-875-2

Local History Journals

The Birmingham Historian	Published by Birmingham and District Association of Local History Societies (articles of local interest, listings of sources, new publications and acquisitions, information about societies active in the Birmingham area, as well as courses and lectures). More information from Hon Secretary P C Baird, c/o Local Studies Dept, Central Library, Chamberlain Square, B3 3HQ Tel: 021 235 4220
The Local Historian	Journal of the British Association for Local History, The Mill, Manager's House, Cromford Mill, Matlock, DE4 3RQ
Local History	Published by Susan and Robert Howard, 3 Devonshire Promenade, Lenton, Notts N67 2DS (National magazine style journal with articles, listings, reviews and news).